# TRANSFORMATION

## Champ

### THE STORY OF

### MY $80,000 SIX-PACK

**NINA NAM**

Editing: Nancy Pile www.zoowrite.com
Cover design: www.ebooklaunch.com
Formatting: Jen Henderson www.wildwordsformatting.com

## DISCLAIMER

The information in this book is not meant to replace the advice of a medical professional. Please consult a licensed physician in matters relating to your health and particularly with respect to symptoms that may require diagnosis or medical attention.

If you choose to attempt any of the methods mentioned in this book, the author advises you to take full responsibility for your safety and know your limits. The author is not liable for any damages or negative consequences from any treatment, action, application, or preparation to any person reading or following the information in this book.

The author shall not be liable for any physical, psychological, emotional, financial, or commercial damages, including but not limited to, special, incidental, consequential, or other damages to the readers of this book.

This book is a memoir. It reflects the author's present recollections of experiences over time to the best of her knowledge. Most names and characteristics have been changed to protect privacy and to prevent unforeseen conflicts, some events have been compressed, and some dialogue has been recreated. The content of this book is the sole expression and opinion of the author.

I won $80,000 as the grand prize winner of Bodybuilding.com's annual 12-week Transformation Challenge amongst 57,300+ people. [1]

After that happened, I went about my normal life. Two years later, a famous psychic advised me to begin writing this memoir. I decided it would be worth it for two reasons:

First, to fire you up! You are meant for great success. Expect miracles, experiences beyond your wildest dreams. Pray to let go of your own limited understanding and let in the abundance of God, the Universe, whatever you want to call it. Whatever struggles you have now, however effed up it is . . . trust there is a greater purpose for you. Everyone we admire has a story about how they got through intense sheeit. Hang in there no matter how hard it gets, because great things are coming. The optimist always wins big.

Second, to show the whole truth behind one champion's quick transformation: the good, the bad, and the ugly.

This is not a guide on how to lose weight fast. And there is no daily workout and meal plan, but I do my best to provide what details I can without getting sued.

If your goal is to win that same contest, then get what you can from here and find a coach who has helped others transform and believes in you. But, ultimately—YOU know your body better than anyone.

FYI I'm not currently a certified trainer, dietician, or doctor. I'm just a psycho who started off wanting to win a lot of cash by getting shredded fast. None of what I share is a recommendation; some of it's not safe. I hesitated to reveal everything, but my mom encouraged me, "Show them everything. You were crazy, so you did crazy things." So, here we go—owwwwww!

Thank you so much for reading. I hope you get everything you want out of it. Ask me anything on Instagram @theninanam. Stay updated on my events, workout classes, and other shenanigans: www.ninanam.com

*To all who wanna smash through it all.*

*Be ye transformed by the renewing of your mind.*

—Romans 12:2

# TABLE OF CONTENTS

## *Introduction*

# JUST SMASH
# THROUGH IT ALL

> *Every adversity, every failure,
> and every heartache carries with it the
> seed of an equivalent or a greater benefit.*
>
> **—from Think and Grow Rich
> by Napoleon Hill**

I don't even like lifting weights, running, and almost everything I did to win the 2015 Bodybuilding.com Transformation Challenge. I only did it because I wanted the money and the body, in the beginning. So, I did every planned friggin' exhausting workout and ate every planned tasteless or straight-up nasty meal, pill, and powder for three consecutive months, no matter how I felt. It was the hardest thing I'd ever done in my life. I didn't break any rules or go off-plan, ever. This miracle was possible for two reasons: FAITH—I believed I had a real chance at winning, I trusted God, I knew deep in my heart that if I stayed committed, it would be worth it—and I stayed fiercely FOCUSED. My story is about the power of FAITH and FOCUS.

As the days went on, my FAITH and FOCUS intensified and I became obsessed, which resulted in a big win at a time in my life when I really needed it. At the time when I did the contest, I was living in a nice apartment that no one would guess was low-income housing, just a five-minute walk to the ocean in beautiful Santa Monica with organic stores everywhere, fancy dogs, and chiseled six-packs jogging on every other block. I had a decent car and nothing was stopping me from living a fulfilling life, that is nothing . . . but me.

I felt like a loser, a phony pretending to be doing OK. After ten years of half-assedly pursuing acting, I only had a handful of credits: three national commercials with my voice deleted out of all of them, a few print ads that I never got to see, and a split second of me saying, "Cheers!" in a big movie.

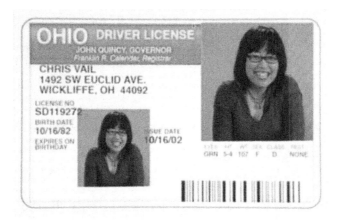

*A clip of me from my first movie role as "Fake ID Kid." How fitting.²*

*My favorite gig.³ I love making pretty faces.*

I loved acting, but I didn't have the thick skin and unstoppable fire for it. The endless rejections felt personal. I repeatedly told myself: "If I was prettier . . .,"

"If I was thinner . . .," or "If I was smarter or funnier, I would have gotten that gig." I didn't put in the necessary hundreds of hours of hard work to strengthen my acting, which would have built a foundation of confidence, or at least made me feel that I was good enough as a performer. Instead, I was hoping my acting dream would come easily, which led to me continuing to project my insecurities. And my self-worth continued shrinking.

With negative thoughts come more negative thoughts. Every new "survival" job reinforced that I was a loser. I guess I'm only good enough for: making and delivering cheap-ass sandwiches; cleaning off tables for celebrities at a high-end sushi restaurant; driving drunk people home at 3am on weekends (that includes providing a throw-up bag, helping them put their shoes back on, and carrying their wobbly-ass bodies to their doorstep—for women . . . for the guys, I'd just shove them out of my car, just kidding, not really); selling alcohol in a cheap tight dress with a high slit in the back as I stood in front of the whiskey section at ghetto Korean grocery stores (I made sure to wear stockings as thick as yoga pants. As an extra insurance against perverts, I wore a business suit jacket and my mom's old dust-encrusted marshmallow nurse shoes, instead of the required sexy heels. As hard as I tried to avoid any Koreans I might know, I ran into my dad, my grandma on my dad's side, my grandpa on my dad's side, my aunt, my uncle, my cousin, another cousin, an old friend, all at separate times, and each looked at me, horrified, like I was some prostitute. They pitied my pathetic career moves. I've quit jobs on the first day of working, others after a few weeks; no matter what though, I was done within several months of starting a job.

An insensitive friend who'd been at her same unfulfilling job for more years than she was proud to admit, laughed in front of a group of mutual friends, "What job hasn't Nina applied for?!" *At least I have the guts to leave a dumb job*, I thought. But her words stung.

I insanely resented working at lame survival jobs. But it was the only way I knew how to have a flexible schedule to attend auditions at any time of the day. I considered putting my acting career on hold in order to be a postal worker, a nurse, or a police officer—legit, respectable stable jobs that would end this pathetic pattern of begging for money from my parents whenever I was friggin' broke, which was a little too often. But I just couldn't see myself keeping those jobs, even if I were to invest a lot of time and money into them.

I almost completed an accelerated emergency medical technician program, until the reality of what might happen on a late-night shift in an ambulance really hit me. I thought working as an assistant to casting directors in the movie business would be a good choice, but after a fun brief stint of hiring a bunch of my friends and family as extras, I got laid off. Extras get paid so much more than you'd think, so I even tried that. But being a background extra on movie sets amongst hundreds of weirdos and wannabes made me fear for my sanity.

Whatever I tried felt like the wrong turn. And it killed me inside to feel so lost for so long. Ten years of making no progress in my career and no personal sense of achievement. I didn't have any goals that excited me. I didn't know what I really wanted, except for the occasional gung-ho desire to lose weight. I was often frustrated, angry, or crying.

I was getting annoyed at myself: the same complaints, the same uneventful day-to-day living. Maybe I had serious issues, so I googled it: depression, what's wrong with me, quarter-life crisis. Maybe I was so mentally ill that I didn't know I was mentally ill! That must be why my family gravely worried about my future. No, I was just different, I hated settling for predictable, boring, and "normal" . . . right?

I admired risk-takers. But what risk was I taking? Why wasn't I able to decide on anything new? Why wasn't something pulling me to change? I've watched many great motivational YouTube videos, but I didn't act any different after they were over.

I didn't know what the heck to do. I went back to Berkeley twice when I had both quarter-life crises, feeling like a failure whose best bet was to finish a sorry degree in theatre arts (a joke on campus; maybe they all knew I had to act like a tree in front of my class) that I'd started years earlier as an undergrad. But I couldn't stand even a minute of listening to an old fart professor blaming Hollywood as racist because she didn't become famous, or cringing as I read a few sentences about ancient theatrical acting in Greece. My heart kept taking me back to LA.

I felt like a burden to those close to me. They saw me struggling and they aggressively offered their best solutions: my mom begged me to join the military, my dad wanted me to work for his construction company, my aunt tried to bribe me into her real estate business, my lawyer sister yelled at me to just get a real job already! Even neighbors and strangers wanted to tell me how to live my life. I was sick of taking everybody's two cents.

I hated telling people I was pursuing acting so much that I eventually stopped talking about it. I wanted to be successful already, be a powerful actress, what I thought was a badass somebody. Definitely not a pathetic 30-year-old wannabe actress.

I knew I was so much better than all this, but was I? *Maybe I'm not that interesting. Maybe I'm not good enough to deserve the kind of life I want.* I was definitely not thin enough according to two very successful talent managers who both rejected me. One of them was known for having a slew of up-and-coming hot young actors, her top client was *the* Superman in the latest Superman movie. The first thing she said was, "You look like you're hiding something. Lift up your shirt and come closer to me." I wasn't trying to hide my belly! I just like baggy shirts! And I wasn't interviewing to be some model, so what the heck? I sucked in my flab slightly, careful that she didn't notice my effort.

Intimidating like Judge Judy, she proclaimed, "You're competing with girls that are a size zero. Unless you want to be the fat funny girl. But you can't be in-between like this. If you're serious about acting, come back to me after you lose the weight. You're cute, but you're starting late."

I didn't know how to respond. *She called me sort-of fat, but at least she called me cute, but she also called me old, but at least she said I could come back, but that means she doesn't think I'm good enough to work as an actress right now just because of the flab she saw only when I lifted my shirt?*

By the time I got in my car, I burst into a broken fire hydrant of tears. I shouldn't have lifted my stupid shirt for her. I shouldn't have let her talk to me like that. I should know how to stand up for myself, I should know how to be grounded and strong. I should be better than this . . .

I was a nobody beggarly actress at the mercy of someone's opinion of me, and I was bitter as hell. But mostly, I was angry at myself. Sometimes it was a full-on rage at this stupid stupid life I created. (Two "stupids" for emphasis.) I was like a pissed-off hamster furiously spinning in my stupid wheel, angry that it was getting me nowhere but continuing that pointless, angry sprint to nowhere anyway. Full-on rage at the stupid wheel I'd stayed on for too long. I wasted so much of my life . . . doing what?

So, when I came across Bodybuilding.com's Transformation Challenge, I grabbed it subconsciously and made it into the fight of my life—the fight for my life: *I will prove to myself that I have what it takes to be a success, that I know how to give it my all, that I am much more than this life I have lived so far.*

So, I decided—JUST SMASH THROUGH IT ALL.

## Chapter 1

# TENDER-FACED

> *The man who says he can, and the man*
> *who says he cannot . . . are both right.*
>
> *—Confucius*

It was around midnight in mid-December. I'd eaten a lot of crap, and I felt like crap, as usual after a binge.

There I was again, staying up late, alone in my one-bedroom apartment, stuck with the same 20-ish pounds that found their way back no matter how hard I tried. I know that doesn't even sound so bad, but my food addiction was bad. Ten years of my life revolved around trying to stop binge eating, aka compulsive overeating, but I couldn't stop. I felt hopeless.

When I was in the grips of a binge-eating episode, I wasted between three hours up to an entire day, obsessing and fantasizing about what I wanted to eat—browsing through photos of food online, usually driving to four or more places to pick it all up.

11

An example of a common binge day would look like the following: ordering creamy fettuccine Alfredo and spaghetti with meatballs (pretending it's for me and a friend, not that anyone ever asked). As soon as I gobbled a few forkfuls of each in the car, I was on my way to get a box of chicken McNuggets with sweet and sour sauce, fries, and a Coke to wash it all down in the McDonald's parking lot—all the while making sure the drive-thru guy didn't see any evidence of my semi-eaten pastas. I'd go back to the pastas until I felt grossed out by them. Then the desire to get something super crunchy would take over, so I'd swing by 7-Eleven for a bag of spicy Takis and a bag of sour cream potato chips. Next, dessert—gotta have it. Nothing crazy, just four full-sized Drumstick ice creams from the grocery store. I'd feel so thirsty by that time that I needed to get some ice cold boba, aka "bubble tea." I'd blown it that far, I didn't friggin' care it was another 1,000 calories of sugar.

This cross-town treasure hunt was a fast series of actions. But with every mouthful of food, I could feel time slowing down. So slow that it became peaceful, finally. Someone once said that this was my way of being present because I'd only focus on the sensations of the food. Interesting . . . I thought it was me numbing out, the opposite of being present. In the end, all I wanted was to be in food-coma bliss.

I didn't care how far I had to drive, as long as I got my fix. One time I drove two hours one-way in LA high traffic to get exactly what I was "craving"—the best dim sum. I would never ask a friend to meet with me for a binge like this. It had to be done in private; otherwise I couldn't devour food the way I wanted to without scaring someone. Some days I felt like a "normal person" with no compulsion to eat anything specific, but many days felt out of control.

Sometimes I would quickly throw away the rest of my "binge food" in the kitchen trashcan. A minute later, I'd grab it out and inhale it. The pint of half-finished Häagen-Dazs or part-eaten brownie—into the trash . . . and then into my face.

If I really wanted to force myself to stop overeating, I'd bag up my sugar-dope, walk it outside and toss it in the dumpster. . .But the very next day, I'd buy the same food again, not for the taste, but for that same hit. It didn't matter what it was, as long as it had a lot of white sugar or a lot of white flour, it would temporarily stop my tornado of repetitive negative thoughts and give me a break from my own brain.

It was too uncomfortable to just sit with my thoughts. "I'm a highly sensitive person with lots of intense feelings," I told myself. The easiest way to get relief was to just eat . . . even though it was never worth it. I would get numb for a night or maybe a whole day, then feel mentally, emotionally, and physically worse the next day. I was too friggin' smart to be doing this sheeit over and over again, but I found myself doing it over and over again. It was demoralizing, and I begged God to get me out of that hellhole many times. But I continued to be a slave to that little voice that told me: "Go eat, you'll feel better, just this one time and start your diet tomorrow; it's too hard to eat healthy all the time, you're not dating anyone, it's OK if you're a little chubby; you don't have to be as skinny as a model, go eat what you want" and other manipulative crap.

A few times I just accepted that I would never get better and seriously considered becoming a successful chubby chef known for making the world's most unhealthy craved crap to satisfy every overeater's fattiest, creamiest, sugariest desire, open 24/7 for whenever the compulsion strikes. You want a warm, chewy, thin crêpe, filled with sweet, sweet Nantucket strawberries and Aussie baby bananas, topped with real Madagascar and Mexican vanilla-bean-speckled llama's milk ice cream and ooey-gooey globs of Nutella with a dollop of handmade, thick-whipped cream from heifers in the Pyrénées—all the size of your head—at 3am? You want that sweet, that nasty, that fatty stuff? Just stop by Naughty Nina's! . . .

I was at the mercy of my bingeing impulses, and it was unpredictable. I used to think if I knew the exact trigger and reason, I could stop it before it happened. I knew I used food for times I felt lonely, not good enough, or frustrated about not speaking up for myself. But logic really didn't help. Bingeing was such a deeply ingrained habit that I assumed I was powerless from breaking it.

My family and friends didn't believe me when I said I had a problem with food because on the outside, I physically looked OK. I didn't throw up or over-exercise till I injured myself. And I did much of my crazy eating when no one was looking or late at night.

I missed out on life because of this. I skipped auditions, flaked on friends, cancelled dates—even really hot ones. Either I thought I looked noticeably bloated after a binge, or I just felt so defeated that I couldn't let myself have fun. Making excuses and lies, I preferred to spend an entire day isolated, driving around town bingeing on drive-thru items and takeout, then continuing to eat more junk at home while devising my next diet, reading about how to end overeating, or researching low-cost therapists . . . This was the norm for a decade.

In order to end overeating and control my weight, I invested incredible amounts of money on different trainers, nutritionists, life coaches, therapists, boot camps, hypnotherapists, psychics, juice cleanses, books, CDs, and online courses. I tried free help: blogs by people who'd overcome compulsive overeating, podcasts, YouTube videos of world-renown addict specialists, a 12-step program called Overeaters Anonymous, counseling from church, and before-and-after weight-loss infomercials (two nationwide infomercials that never aired my impressive transformations! I'm sorry to disappoint, I'm no virgin to transformations).

Now looking back, I see that I was looking for someone or something to fix me. But there was nothing to fix, nothing wrong with me. I was desperate to get rid of the intense feelings that I'd created myself. It was like a switch in my brain screaming, "Danger! You're gonna die! Must do what always works: food!"

I wish I would've tried consistently praying, meditating and simply allowing all the thoughts and feelings to exist, instead of trying to get rid of them. But at that time, it just didn't seem like an option. And really, there's no easy or single "answer" for when we're living through a binge.

So, back to that mid-December night—I didn't feel like watching another YouTube video about how to stop binge eating: "Instead of eating, take a walk, call a friend, take a bath." Or the dumbest one: "Throw everything tempting out of the house." Nothing is going to stop an addict from driving at all hours to get what she wants.

That mid-December night I was browsing through YouTube videos of people who'd lost a lot of weight, and I came across someone talking about Bodybuilding.com's Transformation Challenge. The upcoming contest would reward one man and one woman each $80,000 in cash and one "People's Choice" award for $40,000! I always said I would do a transformation contest but only if it was for a lot of money. Pssh—I ain't getting basically nekked for just a few hundreds.

I immediately had to get a good look at the previous year's winner to see what it was gonna take.

Wow! She went from being a tender-faced blimpy librarian into an FBI hot chick in only 12 weeks! Muscular yet feminine, sexy and lean!

Suddenly, I felt competitive. If a tender-faced white girl could do it, I definitely could do it. I know I look like a tender-faced Asian girl, but whatevz . . .

The judges would judge based on photo submissions. It was a worldwide competition, minus a few weird countries like North Korea (they had an unfair advantage because of that do-or-die mentality, not that any of them had any weight to lose. I'm South Korean, I can say these things).

I decided to stop dieting to get skinnier and start eating to look like a badass. Just the thought of looking badass made me feel badass! Bodybuilding sounded really cool all of a sudden, and that money would make it all worth it.

For the first time in my life, I decided to lift super-heavy weights for every part of my body. (I'd actually tried heavy weightlifting the previous year, but only to grow my butt.) Now I was going to grow all my muscles super big! *Aw yeah—I am so ready for this.* Or so I thought . . .

The next day, I was enjoying some snacks with a close relative at her apartment. I excitedly blurted out that I was going to enter this awesome contest.

Her response: a nonchalant "You're not gonna win."

I stood there shocked because the thought of losing had never even crossed my mind. I was only thinking about winning.

"How can you say that?" I was quickly growing into the Hulk.

Apparently, she didn't mean to hurt me, she was just stating an obvious fact:

"Asians don't win those kind of things."

"NEVER speak to me like that again!" I HULK-SMASHED.

I slammed her little apartment door and cried hard in my car. I felt like my teenage-self. *Why couldn't she just say, "Oh, wow, cool, I hope you win," even if she didn't mean it? No, I'd probably still get really mad cuz I'd know she didn't mean it.*

After that, I shared my plans with only three people and, otherwise, kept my mouth shut.

# Chapter 2

# THE SMALLEST PEPPER

> *Be wary of the people no one wants on their team, the ones who are too small, too slow and not very capable. The unwanted have a built-in motivation to do whatever it takes to succeed that those who are picked first do not have.*
>
> **—*from* With Winning in Mind *by Lanny Bassham***

For a big part of my life, I've been a fighter, sometimes because I had to be; other times because I wanted to be.

In elementary school, I was the one the picked-on kid picked on. He was a tall, big-boned, baby face. I was at a healthy weight, but shorter than most of my peers.

"Nina, let me see your feet, do they smell?" Nothing traumatizing, but everyone would laugh, and I'd feel separated and less than. I would stay quiet and wish I could disappear.

In physical education (PE), he and I were always the last to finish the mile run. Sometimes he would beat me and then smile so big, right in my face. To make it worse, the teacher would send the fastest runner to go find me and motivate me. I hated PE, and I sucked at basically everything.

The picked-on kid always got picked before me for team sports, and then I would get picked last by default; I was the only one left. In softball, I got hit so hard in the right eye that I saw stars. In basketball, I remember I miraculously got the ball and ended up scoring—for the first time ever! . . . For the other team. *Oh, so that's why my teammates were yelling at me* . . . In thumb wars—this was an actual thing our teacher made us do—I thought it was a warm-up, so I lost to an obnoxious girl who screamed with joy having beat me. *Ugh, Nina! Who has a warm-up for thumb wars?!*

In fifth grade, the tallest girl with big boobs taunted me in front of everyone, "Nina doesn't even wear a bra!" I didn't know what a bra was for. I curled into myself like a roly-poly. This is the innocent phase of my life, when I just took the blows, the snickers, and the titters.

The only times I felt safe were during breaks when I played with the other quiet girls. We were pretty badass at parallel bars, Chinese jump rope, and tether-ball—wish one of those was in PE so that we could've kicked some major ass.

*How could anyone bully this innocent face? A little before I became a cussing machine gun.*

In seventh grade, I picked up a few fighting skills. I had to. PE became hell because of three mean-looking skater boys with spikey hair. One time on a mile run, when we were out of the teacher's sight, they took turns throwing pieces of ripped car tires at me. I was lucky not to get hit, but I couldn't outrun them or my mile time: 12 minutes.

This tough black girl used to struggle alongside me and would protect me by cussing out the skaters. But most days she didn't come to school, so I adopted cussing just like her. One of those boys spit gum in my hair, and I spit back with regular spit in his hair—then I got in trouble. The one that supposedly liked me a lot poured sand down the back of my shirt. Wow, I didn't know how to react to his love. The teacher knew all this happened and didn't do sheeit.

During lunch, sitting on the grass with my nerdy friends, the good-looking popular boys came over to throw a stupid note to me that said, "I love you Nina." When I opened it, they laughed so hard. I jumped up pissed. "Get the fuck away!" I shouted, throwing the note back at them, but it floated pretty much back to where they'd thrown it at me. They kept laughing as they happily walked off.

My uncool friends were picked on more often than I was, but they usually kept quiet and tried to walk away from situations. Any boy who dared to bully my friends was gonna hear it from me. I became a cussing machine gun. It didn't stop the bullying, but at least I started speaking up. "What the FUCK did you say? You should shut the FUCK up, you FUCKIN' jerk! Who the FUCK do you think you are? You FUCKIN' stupid ass mean piece of SHIT. You better never FUCKIN' talk to my friend like that again." "Fuck you," a bully might say in response, and I'd have to out-fuck them and say, "NO, F-U-U-U-CK YOU!!!" My mom used to say the smallest pepper is the spiciest . . .

I even pushed that picked-on big-boned bully, yeah, the one back from elementary school. Top five best moments of my life! I was 5'2" (still am, on a good day), and he was half a torso taller than me. After years of his taunting, I had enough. He was walking behind me, doing his usual routine: smiling and making fun of me, loud enough for everyone to hear: "Nina Nina Bo Bina, Banana Fana Fo Fina, Gross Nina!" I quickly spun around and shoved him so hard he fell backwards and clogged the entire doorway causing the other kids to yell impatiently at him to move out of the way. He struggled to get up for a while. It felt good to fight back. I might not be a perfect role model for middle school students, but scrappy badass kids are cool.

One day I felt gusty, I was gonna prove that I was not a loser anymore—this was in ninth grade. I was standing in my old baggy shirt and khaki boy shorts at the edge of the popular kids' lunch area, daring myself to get accepted into the group. I walked up to the three most popular girls in school that resembled the clique from the movie *Mean Girls*—makeup, expensive short skirts, and all. Before I even opened my mouth, they all turned around in unison and glided away from me. The worst part was, as I stood there dumbfounded, I felt little rocks being thrown at my head. I didn't want to look even stupider by frantically turning around to figure out where they were coming from, so I speed-walked away until I didn't feel the rocks anymore, vowing to never be humiliated like that again.

Crushed, I started hiding in classrooms far from the popular group, pretending I had a lot of homework, and hiding in bathrooms during breaks to avoid being seen. I even pulled away from my dorky friends. It was safer and easier that way.

Skip to my eleventh grade year. I could've been destroyed by what my high school guidance counselor, the one who is supposed to help students in the college process, told me, "You probably won't get into UC Berkeley, so aim for realistic schools." But I was hell-bent on proving him wrong. *I will get into my dream school.* I decided to ace the rest of my classes, score higher on the SATs, write a *damn* good essay, and create my own *darn* club (yes, my cursing is carefully chosen depending on the intensity of the next word or randomly thrown in to keep you awake), so that I could call myself "president and founder" instead of pipe-dreaming that peers would vote for me for some other position in a club I don't even care about.

Hell yeah, I got into UC Berkeley. More on that later.

I'm sharing all this growing-up stuff, so you can see the dueling forces that were inside me during the transformation competition—on the one hand, I was a longtime fighter, battling anyone and everyone who thought I couldn't do it; on the other, the seeds of feeling like a loser had been planted in me, I was sensitive and afraid, and I doubted myself, many times.

In a bodybuilding contest, it isn't your diet and exercise program that's going to give you an advantage; it's your mind. You need that insane focus, that never-never-never-give-up mentality, and you need to want to go farther than anyone else. I promised myself before I began the contest: *I won't give up, no matter how much it sucks*. Before the contest even began, I sent a short email to my coach: *"I'm in it to win it."*

*Fighter or loser—prove what you are. PROVE IT! Do you really have what it takes? This is your chance to give it all you've got. Right here, right now.* These thoughts were like whips on an already beaten body. I had a deeply personal emotional need to win. I couldn't have won if I'd been already content with my life. I wouldn't have had the fuel to plow through so aggressively. I used all the pain and frustration of everything that had built up to that point, to grit my teeth and friggin' grind. G-R-I-N-D.

# Chapter 3

# LITTLE SHEEIT,
# BIG SHEEIT

*Well-behaved women rarely make history.*

*—Marilyn Monroe*

Since we're digging into this important thing—mindset—we can't forget about family, right? The foundation for my crazy head.

I grew up in the beautiful, comfortable parts of Southern California (Orange County). My hard-working immigrant parents moved from South Korea to the US in their late-twenties, not knowing English, with big dreams of success. My dad finally became his own boss and was one of the pioneers in making fresh Korean yogurt in America, something that became insanely in demand by all major Asian markets.

We were living the American dream: three-story huge home; a backyard the size of a small park that my siblings and I would ride our bikes all over; three nice cars; frequent big dinner parties with friends and relatives; and yearly vacations and amusement park visits.

Our grandparents (on my mom's side) moved in with us to help raise us and care for the house. Though my grandma, Halmunee, had worked in a rice field all her life, she became Americanized fast. She knew how to pick up the phone and say, "NO ENGULEESHEE," loud and clear. Halmunee gained ten pounds from her favorite foods: KFC and Coke. And she cooked spaghetti almost every week. Her meatballs were as big as softballs, a self-taught genius—ain't nobody making meatballs in Korea, she had no reference point! And when she was pickling kimchi, she hand-fed little pieces into my mouth. It was food and love all mixed in one. Ah. (Maybe this is why after one man spoon-fed me on a date, I was hooked on him for a year. My friend thought it was weird. Who's weird, the feeder or the feedee? Bah, she doesn't know love. Or maybe I don't because I'm still single. That's right—single and ready to mingle! You got my ig, right?)

I loved our big family of eight—parents, grandparents, and four kids—I'm the oldest, two little sisters, the youngest is my brother. And we all loved food: two refrigerators and a wall of pantries, packed. We would restock at Costco, getting a cart full of hundreds of dollars' worth of groceries every time. We would restock at Korean grocery stores every week. We ordered delivery usually twice a week. We lived to eat!

I think I loved my dad more than my mom only because he would order an extra bucket of KFC more than she ever did. If we drove through Krispy Kreme, we always bought three huge boxes of doughnuts. If we saw a bagel shop, we grabbed a dozen bagels, regardless of how many we planned on eating. Someone would gobble up the leftovers later that day or microwave it the next day. You never waste food!

To this day I get annoyed by people who say they eat a lot when they don't. We could never be friends. You gotta be honest with me, mang. That's not a typo, mang. My family knew the meaning of "a lot." It meant finishing everything and getting more. And if you were polite, you'd get a third serving to show how much you really appreciated the food. And if you didn't finish your plate, all the adults would nag you to finish it or to give it to them even if they were full.

If you took a quick look, we all looked pretty good. I said "quick" because my dad could suck in his gut for three seconds. My parents didn't know fast food and sodas were unhealthy; they'd grown up in rural areas without many food options, so they gave us all that they could afford. When my grandma from my dad's side first came to the States, she drank ten sodas a day, instead of water, and developed diabetes, even though she was very petite. Surprisingly no one is obese in my family. Being a high-tempered Korean burns a lot of calories.

My parents wanted my siblings and me to be great students and be great at something in addition. They worked long hours and spent a fortune having us try lots of things because they genuinely wanted each of us to have a lifelong hobby and passion. But I had no interest in: Korean traditional dancing, ballet, Tae Kwon Do, golf, violin, guitar, piano, Chinese private lessons, Spanish classes during the summer, summer camps, and especially doing the extra-learning homework that Mom ordered from an evil academic company. Only my mom and other Asian moms kept that company in business. This has to be how I learned to take things into my own hands and how I fine-tuned my fighting spirit, for better or for worse . . .

While my mom was running her acupuncture clinic, I would take peeks at the answer sheets she used to check the extra-learning homework from the evil academic company. Ain't nobody got time for fake homework. I also stole money from her purse to buy candy when she was busy helping patients. If I felt like skipping class in high school, I would give my teacher a forged note the next day, pretending that I was home sick and signed the note exactly how my mom signs. Suckaaahs.

Despite their busy schedules, my parents always showed up for important things related to school or extracurriculars and even for normal projects like building a clay volcano that I would of course procrastinate on doing and my dad would have to work past midnight, oops, I mean—I would have to work past midnight to finish. That's why it looked so good, and I would get an A, duh.

I became really good at going through the motions, doing the bare minimum whenever possible.

Tae Kwon Do was the most physically demanding and the hardest to fake all the way through, so I would beg my grandma to tell Mom that I didn't like it. But my mom kept taking us.

One time, my favorite violin teacher, a very tall, handsome, gay, black man in his thirties, literally had tears welling up in his eyes, saying I was his most talented student and I had the potential to be great but wasted it by not practicing. He was so wrong. I did practice— thirty minutes before he showed up for my lesson. My mom, so frustrated that I hadn't practiced all week, would beg me, "Can you practice at least because you feel sorry about the money that I spent?" I would hang my head low and lie that I was sorry, and I would practice just long enough until she got busy with other things, less than ten minutes, guaranteed.

I was in the school orchestra since middle school, and I was hands down the best at the ghost bow—that's when you barely touch your bow on the strings so that no one can tell you're not playing. You don't need to practice when everyone else is doing it for you.

I ghost-bowed my way all the way to the end of high school. But to get into my dream school, Berkeley, I had to do more extracurriculars to prove that I was well-rounded. I didn't like golf, but it wasn't too hard and I kinda knew how to do it after begrudgingly practicing many hours with the family and a few private lessons. It was easy becoming captain of the girls' varsity golf team because no one else had any lessons at all! And all the girls actually liked me. I could've cared less if we ranked the worst team of Southern California (oh yeah, we were! Even better, because we never felt the pressure to practice hard or win!). Life was good being captain of a team with no expectations.

**Sports** *Spotlight*

## Girls Golf

### Nina Nam

**Year**: Sophomore
**Golf Experience**: 1 year
**Coach's Comments**: "Nam has the best form on the team and seems to have the most experience. She also works hard to help the rest of the team."
**Goals**: "I look forward to playing with the team in competition," Nam said. "We strive to do our best. We also just need to work on our distance, accuracy and concentrate on the course. I personally want to develop myself to an advanced level."

*Check out your girl in the high school newspaper.*
*Can you believe they forgot to mention I was captain? Captain of Bull Sheeiting!*

I loved going to Korean School on Saturdays though. Because four hours of doodling, spacing out to the sound of the teacher, and writing notes to friends was worth the guaranteed lunch at either McDonald's, KFC, or Taco Bell! At McDonald's, I would put fries in my burger and then pour an entire packet of sweet-and-sour sauce all over that, put the bun back on top, and eat it with three more fries with each bite.

My sister hated sharing fries with me. She's so friggin' greedy. I'm the oldest sister and the biggest sister, so I get to eat the mostest!

When I started University of California Berkeley, I was at my highest weight. It happened so gradually over years of eating freely and low physical activity. But, interestingly, I wasn't self-conscious about my weight back then. I didn't diet or emotionally eat. There was no social media, and I rarely looked at magazines or TV.

That was one of the happiest times of my life. I laughed so much. I had many friends, and there were no popular kids or bullies. I didn't give a F--- when I got a "F" in organic chemistry. No, I wasn't on drugs! I was just high on social life for the first time!

We would go out dancing in the city. We'd go out for long walks at 2am for doughnuts. I poured hours into baking cookies and a giant cake for my crush who never even liked me back (. . . until recently when he saw my pictures on Facebook. You ungrateful turd! It's too late and it's called I-look-as-beautiful-as-I-was-back-then-except-now-I-can-draw-my-eyebrows!).

In my third year, I took a DJ-ing class and an acting class, and then honorably withdrew from the university. That's the smart way of dropping out because then you're allowed to come back anytime. It's been over a decade. Don't even start with telling me to go back to school. My mom would give you a high five though. She just reminded me to go back to school again, literally today, as I was writing this, even though I threatened to disown her if she said it one more time. She said she doesn't remember me ever threatening her. Dammit, Mom! You've been disowned at least ten times for the same reason! When are you gonna learn!?

One of the best things that ever happened at Berkeley was falling in love with cardio-kickboxing. I partied in my favorite teacher's class once or twice a week. It was the hardest funnest workout ever.

*Advertisement for the university's group fitness classes. No, I'm not the perfect girl in front. I'm the newb in the glasses with wrists curled in!*

After leaving university, I tried similar classes at various gyms but very inconsistently, sometimes not working out for months at a time. I remember a few times doing light dumbbell workouts from *Self Magazine*, hoping it would make me look like the model that got paid to demonstrate them. I joined a few boot camps for one to three months at a time, maybe committing five times a week, and enjoying friendly competitiveness with the most athletic peeps. But that was only to lose weight fast, and I either got burned out or bored sooner than later.

I tried yoga and pilates at private studios for a few months but, um, expensive. I hired trainers and dumped them almost as soon as I started because I couldn't stick to their reasonable diets. I visited one of Richard Simmons's classes and he thought I was an instructor. I took Chalene Johnson's class once, and she told me to be an instructor. This is because I had good form (unlike the curled wrists in the pic above) and went hard (unbeknownst to them, I was secretly competing with these fitness gurus and their long-time students). I'm not saying this to show off (maybe a little), I just want to explain how even though I was sorely inconsistent with exercise, I can get unexplainably competitive, picking up new exercises quickly and doing them intensely. It's probably because of my parents' wiring my brain (or attempting to) early in life with lots of different physical disciplines, various musical instruments, and several languages mixed the trauma of having never beat anyone in any of those stupid PE sports! See, Mom, all that half-assed work on my part made a difference!

In all seriousness though, I didn't feel that I was particularly great at exercise, I didn't even have anything specific I liked so much that I would do consistently besides the occasional cardio-kickboxing class. Up until my early thirties, I never had a routine. My fitness was messy and sporadic, just like my eating.

# Chapter 4

# WHAT'S THE PLAN, MANG?

*The will must be stronger than the skill.*

*—Muhammad Ali*

I figured out that the Bodybuilding.com Transformation Challenge was not about who lost the most weight, who lifted the most weight, or who ran the fastest on the treadmill. Heck, the fastest I ran on the treadmill was around an 8 mph pace. I knew I would not be the fastest or the strongest. Also I only lost 21 pounds overall in the weeks of the competition, and that's including water weight (which could easily have been 5+ pounds). I knew one fellow competitor who lost around over 50 pounds, but he didn't have a shredded physique by the end, so he didn't win.

Winning the competition was also not about who looked the most amazing in their after-pic (especially if they still looked fit in the before-pic—why you wasting our time? Rolling my eyes).

Who wins? The person who VISUALLY looked "BAD" and then transformed into a BADASS. Who went from ZERO to HERO. The person who showed the most dramatic difference, someone that Bodybuilding.com would put on their website and expect viewers to scream, "WOW, only 12 weeks? Gimme those supplements NOW!"

For this reason, I knew my before-pic had to look as bad as possible—and my after-pic as amazing as possible.

The night before my before-pic, I ate my biggest cheat meal on earth. I ordered from three of my favorite restaurants. And I got all my friends to help me out, their names were: Sugar, Salt, Dairy and Liquids. I devoured a burrito the size of my forearm—full of rice and beans, guacamole, sour cream, jalapenos, greasy grilled onions, and some pointless veggies; a large bag of salty tortilla chips with two cups of salsa; an extra-large portion of fries with several packets of ketchup; a palm-sized piece of carrot cake; a chocolate chip cookie as big as my hand spread-out; a large Coke; and water 'til my tummy felt like exploding. This served a dual purpose: (1) a reward for committing to three months of dieting and (2) to look bloated to the max for the before-pic. It's not cheating to eat a crapload of food the night before; others do it like it's their last meal on earth, too. But I may have done it better, wink face.

While I wasn't planning on having any cheat meals during the three months of the competition, upon reading that a few cheat meals could result in speeding up your metabolism temporarily, I let myself have three reasonably-sized cheat meals early in the competition.

In the before-pic I intentionally wore a sports bra and shorts that were a little too small, so they dug into my soft spots, creating chubby rolls on my back and accentuating my flabulousness. I didn't smile because no one smiles in before-pictures. (But that's so predictable. Now I wish I had smiled in my before-pic. I should've smiled in the before-picture and then looked sad in the after-pic. Do you think I would've still won?)

That miserable look I had on my face was real, though. No acting there.

To maximize my transformation, I submitted the before-pic as early as possible and the after-pic as late as possible. This gave me a total of 14 weeks even though technically the competition is advertised as 12 weeks. It's all in the details!

I stumbled upon my coach, Beanstalk, on Facebook. Enamored by her great skin, sparkly eyes, and sexy strong physique, I started reading her posts. They were funny and sassy; I was instantly a fangirl! I even flew out to Canada for the first time, just to meet her in person at the Veg Expo. This was before I'd thought of competing at all. Years previously, I'd tried veganism for two weeks, and my skin looked its best and my bowel movements were highly satisfying (the two most important things in life). But my carnivorous desires got the best of me, and I was turned off by vegans who demonized meat eaters as murderers or those who showed off their strange stringy muscles. Beanstalk inspired me to try being vegan again. She had been vegan her whole life and won two bikini competitions against many meat eaters. I trusted her and half a year later I emailed her, asking if she'd coach me.

We communicated everything via email, about every few days over the course of the competition. I hoped a vegan diet would help with faster muscle recovery because it's less acidic compared to a meat-filled diet. Perhaps I would even lose weight faster as a vegan! I was curious to see.

My meal plan (to describe it very generally) went like this: 6 mini-meals, along with 2–4 protein shakes a day. I ate every 3-ish hours and consumed a limited variety of food. (Remember, the info here is not a recommendation of how to eat for health or for your competition. Please consult your doctor, coach, or nutritionist who has your unique body and needs in mind.)

## MY COMPETITION FOOD LIST

- steel-cut oats
- yams/sweet potatoes
- white rice
- quinoa
- tempeh
- tofu, tofu skins/yuba (only in the first half of the competition)
- beans
- fruits (berries, pears, pineapples, grapefruits)
- vegetables (broccoli, spinach, green beans, carrots, red peppers, cucumbers, asparagus)
- Udo's oil—I chose this as my main source of fat because it contains a variety of fats; supposedly helps with muscle recovery and brain function
- lemons—fresh-squeezed in warm water with probiotics upon awakening
- apple cider vinegar—helps with weight loss and digestion, alkalizes body
- cayenne pepper
- pink Himalayan salt

*Note:* I tried to eat all organic

I kept supplements to a minimum and refused to take mysterious chemical-laden stuff that sped up my heart rate. Other contestants used coffee, pre-workout drinks, creatine, and/or fat burners to increase energy, muscle growth, and/or speed up weight loss, but I did not. I wanted to rely on my own energy and use my own hacks that did not involve ingesting questionable ingredients. I know, some of my own hacks seem questionable too, but we all have our own logic (or lack there of . . .).

## SUPPLEMENTS

- a multivitamin for active women—mine had a little green tea extract
- vitamin B-12
- vitamin C—when I got sick
- BCAAs—muscle repair and performance, possibly staved off hunger and gave me a tiny bit more energy to continue working out, but don't quote me on that
- glutamine—helps relieve soreness
- glucosamine MSM & CMO—joint supplement to relieve the impact on my knees during running
- digestive enzymes—helps digest tough veggies, beans, big cheat meals
- protein powder—vegan, chocolate-flavored first month; last two months, plain hemp (tastes like grainy mud) and brown rice (you would think this would taste alright, but it might as well be chalk)
- chlorella, spirulina—each have 6 grams of protein per tablespoon and very little calories. Mixed both into protein shakes using a Vitamix to mix it in thoroughly
- probiotics—improves digestion and makes great poops aka flatter tummy
- almond milk—enjoyed this with protein powders for a month; after that strictly water
- no flavored water or flavored supplements, no gum—I didn't want to crave sweets or create a desire to eat more

Overall, I think I gained 2 pounds or less of muscle from start to finish of the competition. Before and after the competition, I paid a small fee at a local clinic to measure my body fat, muscle mass, etc., by standing barefoot on a metal machine and holding onto metal rods. But these things are never a hundred percent accurate (my numbers are a best estimate). When you eat so little and exercise so much in order to lean out, it's normal to lose some muscle. Some people think a vegan diet accelerates muscle loss, but during those three months, I believe I kept almost all of the muscles I already had and added a tiny bit here and there.

## WORKOUTS

Just to be very clear: The goal of the exercise and meal plan Beanstalk helped to develop was to lean out my whole body while maintaining as much muscle as possible. There wasn't time to pack on a lot of new muscle, as most of the time was needed to focus on losing fat to reveal what muscles I did have and to fine-tune some muscles at the end.

Beanstalk used the exact workouts and diet she'd created to win her competitions as a foundation for me, but she tweaked exercises and amounts of food according to my weekly progress pics. For example: My shoulder muscles were barely noticeable, so she added more shoulder workouts; my thighs needed more toning, so she added more running; and my body is sensitive to carbs, so she kept them low for most of the time, so I'd quickly lean out (and nearly die).

My workout routine changed about every month. And I never worked out with my trainer by my side.

Before every cardio and every lifting session, I would warm up on the treadmill for five minutes, do a few dynamic stretches, and roll out some knots and tight spots with a PVC pipe (cheaper and more intense than a styrofoam roller).

After every cardio and every lifting session, I had a 30-minute cool-down, consisting of time slowing down on the treadmill for a few minutes, rolling out knots and tight spots again with the PVC pipe, and static stretching (thoroughly holding each stretch for 30-45 seconds or longer if needed). I never rushed those 30-ish minutes. Many people do too little stretching or skip it altogether, thinking they're saving time or it's not a big deal. I believe it's crucial for flexibility, preventing injuries, having aesthetically-pleasing-looking muscles, and alleviating soreness so that I could get back to working out hard again.

## CARDIO

I did high intensity interval training (HIIT) cardio on an empty stomach about 6 times a week with each section lasting thirty to sixty minutes. The reason I did "fasted HIIT cardio" immediately upon awakening is that many believe it burns more fat compared to doing it after you've eaten one or more meals.

I switched up my exercises to keep my body guessing and give it no chance to get comfortable. Sometimes I'd be on a treadmill varying the incline and speed. I prioritized speed over incline on the treadmill for the purpose of leaning out. I'd mix in walking lunges and side shuffles on the treadmill, and then quickly get off for wide and narrow squats or high knees. Sometimes I'd be on a stationary bike varying the resistance and speed, butt up (never seated). Sometimes I'd use the Stairmaster, stepping forward and backward, varying the speed. Other times I'd do body weight only like jump squats and stationary lunges.

## WEIGHTLIFTING

Each week I did four to five weightlifting sessions that lasted 1-2.5 hours, in the afternoon or evening. I'd do four or five sets (or rounds) of 15–25 reps and sometimes add super sets and even triple sets to make these weightlifting sessions more cardio-based in order to really lean out. A little background on the terminology: a "super set" is when you do two exercises in a row without stopping to make a complete set. A "triple set" is three exercises in a row. I aimed to rest for 60 second in between sets.

Typically, I'd work my lower body about 3 times a week and upper body about 3 times a week. In order to maximize the workout, I lifted as heavy as possible while still maintaining good form and keeping my heart rate up. My maximum for leg extensions (using both quads) was 85 pounds; squats on the Smith machine at 75 pounds; bicep curls at 20 pounds in each hand; and deadlifts at 45-pound dumbbells in each hand (with much needed wrist wraps to give support to my insufficient grip strength). Not too crazy, right?

Many times, I was not able to maintain my max with perfect form all the way to the final rep of an exercise, so mid-exercise I would quickly grab lighter weights or continue taking off weights until I finished.

## OUTFIT OF A PSYCHO ON A TYPICAL DAY AT THE GYM

It's sweaty and torturous enough to run fast on an incline or lift as heavy as possible. Imagine working out beast-mode wearing this (listed in the order of how I dressed):

*A typical outfit. Why you looking at my face rolls?*

- Vaseline or Sweet Sweat—thickly coated on abs, thighs, and upper arms
- Saran wrap—around abs and thighs, two times around
- tank top
- tight corset
- shirt (you can't see it in the pic, but then again, you can't see or feel half the sheeit I'm tryin' to display here)
- sweater
- sweat-inducing neoprene beanie—the head releases 60% of body heat (sometimes an extra hat)
- tight calf compression sleeves
- compression leggings
- gloves—despite so much sweating, my fingers were unbearably freezing cold due to the diet

## MY HACKS

*Corsets*—some say it's been done ages ago and is effective in shrinking the waist; others say it's unhealthy or it could damage your organs; I say—Gimme six of 'em! Some for cardio, some for weights and abs (softer material to perform ab moves), some for throughout the rest of the day and even to bed.

Sometimes it was difficult to breathe while running uphill in a tight corset. When you (perhaps stupidly!) force yourself to wear an even tighter corset to bed, you experience sudden sharp pains in your ribs and your thighs feel slightly numb due to corset-induced blood circulation problems.

Eventually my body gave up on hinting that something was wrong, and I honestly did not feel much discomfort at all. Then I wore smaller sizes as I kept losing weight.

I'm not sure how much smaller the corset made my waist compared to if I hadn't used it at all, but at least it made my belly and back sweat a lot—two thumbs up!

*FAR-infrared heated bed*—while it's called a "bed," it's literally a sleeping bag. Supposedly spending time in one helps with inflammation, joint pain, muscle soreness, and weight loss. According to Shapehouse.com, 55 minutes of sizzling like a juicy sausage in one of these sacks burns between 800 and 1,600 calories. If that isn't enough of an incentive, Lady Gaga posted on Instagram that infrared saunas help her tremendously post-performance (and she's a beast on stage).

It gradually heats up to 158°F. If it felt unbearably hot, I'd roll around within the enclosed sleeping bag like a shish kabob, but I only opened a crack once! I made sure the heat didn't escape from the neck hole and that my sweat-inducing beanie was on tightly. I pulled the infrared beams close to my abs, thighs, and arms.

Afterwards, I'd sleep well. Most importantly, it defrosted my freezing fingers, so that alone made it worth it.

At first, I went to infrared sauna beds once a week-ish, then upped it to several times a week, and finally consecutive days near the very end of the competition. A couple times I went twice a day when management didn't notice. Despite drinking 1.5–2 gallons of water a day, I woke up insanely thirsty.

Even towards the end of the competition, when I was severely reducing water intake and dehydrating myself with dandelion root extract, I still did the infrared sauna. This is one of the things I warned you is not safe to do.

*Special massages*—not from a sexy man, you naughty reader, you. About a month away from the deadline, I tried a unique massage in fancy Beverly Hills, that supposedly helps bodybuilders create more definition in their muscles, looking fuller and popping more.

Frustrated, the masseuse complained to me, "You have too much fat for me to know where to separate the muscles!" I was obviously not as lean as the professional bodybuilders she was accustomed to seeing.

I calmly and desperately asked, "Can you please try to help me with my abs and thighs?"

I learned her technique right away: Dig so hard into those muscle-defining lines till you scream. She was breaking up tight fascia (the thin membrane that encases the muscles) which may help muscle separation look deeper and more obvious. After I paid almost $200 for a 50-minute session, I resolved to do it myself.

I discovered guashua, an ancient Chinese technique to release toxins and improve circulation by using a smooth piece of buffalo bone to scrape your face and body. My mom actually used it to gently contour her face and prevent wrinkles. Somehow I saw her nightly beautifying regimen as a perfect tool for painfully digging into my six-pack and thighs. I bruised myself for 30 minutes every night with buffalo bones of varying shapes. They probably weren't even real bones or buffalo; but hey, it was as painful as that masseuse and way cheaper. The night prior to my after-pic, I was bruised pretty good, but the spray tan hid most of it on picture day.

For lubrication, I guashua-ed with coconut oil and different cellulite-reducing serums. I used generous globs of pricey products and let them sting and sink in overnight. Also, sometimes before going to sleep I applied cellulite-reducing pads on my inner thighs. Who knows what was in them, but I'd wait out the stinging as much as I could before I tore them off to finally fall asleep in my corset. A beast's gotta do . . .

# Chapter 5

# FOCUS POCUS

> *The successful warrior is the average man with laser-like focus.*
>
> *—Bruce Lee*

Teenee, a coworker, once told me that she always wanted to be a sheriff but that she figured, "If it's meant to be, it's meant to be." So, since it wasn't happening, it must not be meant to be.

My response: "No, Teenee! If you want to be a sheriff, you gotta work hard for it, and I know you can do it."

"But it's too hard to pass the physical test because my foot is still out of whack from that bad surgery two years ago," Teenee explained.

I immediately showed her a YouTube video of the motivational speaker Nick Vujicic. He's a guy with no arms or legs, just one little floppy appendage where his leg should be that he jokingly refers to as his "chicken

57

wing." In the video, he's energetically walking around a stage, his entire face beaming, and telling kids to believe how perfect they are. CUT TO: Vujicic happily driving a boat, a car . . .

Teenee asked, "How the hell does he do all that?"

"Because he didn't say, 'If it's meant to be, it's meant to be.' He's got barely half a foot, but you got two whole feet, yet you're waiting.'"

Come on, Teenee . . .

And . . . come on, Nina!

The diet was so intense and the workouts so demanding, that my energy level was usually low. I was desperate to save my energy only for my workouts. So I had to stay FOCUSED on only what was absolutely necessary.

One night, early on in the competition, when I was sweating my balls off in the infrared bed, and my mind was beat and wandering, I had a fear vision of a witch coming to me, ready to cast on me the scariest of all spells: "You, The Nina Nam, will stay the same as you were before the competition for the rest of your days— binge-eating, non-committing, part-time-job hustling, angry, feeling ugly—for decades to come! Heeeee!"

In that infrared oven-bag of perspiration, I begged aloud, "Pretty witch, please give me FOCUS POCUS. Give me insane focus to get out of my stupid life, to experience abundance and success, to see and do things that are beyond my wildest dreams. Please, please, I beseech you!"

OK—this cheezy hallucination never happened. My point is to emphasize FOCUS. My focus was on outworking everybody, doing things that they were not willing to do: working less (so, getting paid less), investing all my money into the competition (not being cheap), sleeping lots, avoiding distractions/pleasures/socializing (dating? What's that?!), and conserving energy for the workouts and competition-related planning. I was determined to be more focused than anyone else.

In order to stick to my plan, I said NO a lot. I fiercely protected my food, my time, and my mind. There was no time to be a people pleaser, the way I used to be. I was extremely selfish: I had to win that 80 grand and get that bod.

For one of my cheat meals, early on in the competition, I invited my friend Muppet to enjoy it with me. As I was savoring my vegan burger, I noticed he was taunting me with one of my French fries. He thought it would be so funny and cute to steal one. My blood-curdling scream scared him like he was Bambi caught in the headlights of a Nina Humvee. In that moment I saw myself—it was an out-of-body experience—at first reaching for that fry, but then suddenly, viciously slapping it out of his hand. Neither of us got to eat it.

It made no sense that I would slap the fry out of Muppet's hand, I wanted to eat it, dammit! But my deep primal impulse got the best of me, attacking this intruder who dared to steal my food. It was as confusing and disturbing as when a mother gerbil eats her own sick babies.

Muppet and I then laughed about how silly we were, but we both knew that I was now officially: a psycho.

I never invited him to eat with me again for the rest of the competition, but don't worry—we stayed close friends.


A few weeks in, my dad made a surprise visit.

"Hey, let me treat you to something really yummy today! Soup Plantation? No, let's go all out—Korean BBQ!"

He was smiling and rubbing his hands together, excited to have a spontaneous feast with me.

Normally, I would have jumped in the car before he'd finished talking. But my response today: "No, Appa, I have to eat what I made today."

"Eat it later. Come on, let's go!"

"Appa, remember I'm doing a competition? I have to follow the meal plan."

He furrowed his brows, concerned, and voiced, "It's not good to diet, it's not a good way to live like that."

"Appa, it's a competition! Do you want me to lose?" I asked, unflinching.

"One time won't make a difference," he insisted.

"You want me to lose," I insisted back.

I had to say it like that to make him give up, finally.

I saw every atom of food not on my plan as instant losing. Nothing tempted me during the competition. I never craved anything, I was never even hungry. This was very unlike me, eating like a mechanical masticator. God was definitely helping me because I never before could stay on any diet for that long without sabotaging my efforts.

I usually worked alone as a part-time administrative assistant for the city. But I was asked to help out in the Section 8 Housing Department for a little bit. A few of us sat side by side for 8 hours straight sorting through old paperwork and scanning papers onto the computers. No wonder food was the highlight for these bored office workers. But I ain't scurred of no food-pushers.

One day, my coworker, Katrina, brought a variety of cookies, including watermelon Oreos. Maybe that's why I wasn't tempted. In all honesty, the old Nina would've tried one of each cookie and then taken more of the ones she liked.

Katrina urged, "Nina, these are so good, take as many as you want!"

I explained politely, "Thank you, Kat, but I can't because of the competition I'm doing."

"Just lick them then," she dared.

Oh, you are oh-ho-ho-ho-so smart and funny!

I gave her the finger, I mean a fake laugh, brushing her off, "You're so cray," and casually continued stapling.

I did a double take. The bish was still sitting there staring at me, hoping to see me crack!

I just awkwardly smiled and kept working, thinking I better report this work harassment cuz that's some twisted sheeit, mang . . .

I carried around a pricey heavy-duty meal prep bag, glued to my hip. I never let anyone touch it, like a mamma bear with her cub. Every ingredient was measured and weighed precisely. It was the first time I packed containers, ice bags, and protein shakers.

*A pretty face for you! Oh, and my "nuclear football."*

After working with Kat and them housing department zombies, I went back to the comfort of my own office as an administrative assistant for a little community park with some tennis courts. I worked alone there, i.e., clear of food-pushers. It was the easiest, quietest, great-paying job for a few days a week, five-hour shifts. Besides checking in tennis patrons and answering calls, I spent a good chunk of time reading articles about bodybuilding and assisting Airbnb guests (my other job). Once in awhile, I was interrupted by a homeless person pooping on the courts or an old man asking me to play tennis with him. But otherwise, it was a piece of cake. Or shall I say, a piece of asparagus . . .?

One day I dropped an asparagus on the floor at the tennis office. Those tiles have never been mopped for at least 20 years, I bet you a thousand dollars. I quickly snatched my asparagus off the floor, trying hard not to think about what invisible particles got absorbed into its cold, limp, boiled, porous skin: microscopic flecks of dog feces, dead skin cells, asbestos, particles of spider eggs, or blonde nose hairs. Under my breath, I kept repeating, "Ew, ew, ew, ew, ew, ew," as I rushed to the public restroom to rinse it and then pop it in my mouth, barely chewing, swallowing it as fast as possible. The sacrifice!

I ate everything on my meal plan. I saw every bite of food as a step closer to winning. And I did not like most of my food. I avoided microwaving because it brought out the stench of tempeh and asparagus (which I ate a lot of). Don't tell me you like asparagus! Have you tried eating 15 boiled (at times slimy) asparagus spears all in one sitting, with no salt, no pepper, and no oil? I gagged every day, sometimes 3 times over the course of one meal. No exaggeration. These were unavoidable, sudden, intense eye-bulging-brain-out-of-order-anus-tightening dry-heaving episodes. During the last 2 months of the contest, I ate between 30 and 40 asparagus a day. That alone should've earned me $80K.

I did whatever it took to make every meal perfect and of the highest quality. I searched everywhere for high-protein, low-calorie tofu skins, easily driving an hour one way to different grocery stores. Tofu skin (aka yuba or bean curd skin) is the film that forms from boiling soy milk in the process of making tofu. It's chewy and tastes better than tofu, in my opinion. I dug in the back of refrigerators, persistently annoyed managers, and made big special orders (not cheap).

I swiped every credit card and used everything in my bank account for this competition. I spent over twenty grand. You bet I expensed that sheeit!

The most unexpected bill was from the chiropractor the month before I officially began the competition. I avoided seeking help, but I got desperate. I explained to Dr. Cote, "My low back hurts so bad I haven't been able to squat for a week."

Dr. Cote explained that my low back is jammed due to tight hip flexors and hamstrings. He emphasized the importance of stretching for about 45 seconds straight and not sitting for over two hours straight. Tight hip flexors are a common reason why so many people get injured. He fixed me in a few sessions for just under a grand. Worth it.

I fiercely protected my time, especially at the gym. I always wore a hat or a beanie or both, and kept my head down. I started sweating from my corset and extra layers even before the workout began.

I disciplined my eyes to only look at things related to my workout. I walked fast from one exercise to the next, in order to keep my heart rate up and to end the workout ASAP. My fingers were usually freezing all day and their inability to warm up during workouts annoyed me constantly. For some reason they always freeze whenever I go on a diet. Despite being drenched in my own sweat for hours, I never changed clothes during workouts because I did not want to waste any time and break my momentum. But sometimes I'd feel my energy drop so much that I'd eat part of my next meal, before finishing the remaining workout.

One day I was in the middle of speed walking to the next machine when I heard someone call out, "Hey, I know you," a not-so-cute 30-ish-year-old guy smiled, comfortably placing his elbow on a machine, getting ready for a flirty time.

RED ALERT: Time waster.

"Yeah! Hey, gotta work out," I chirped, and left him hanging awkwardly as I swooshed past. He used to be a customer at one of my old jobs. Did I care? No. Do you care? No.

I was a ninja quickly blocking every possible time-waster/focus-snatcher.

*Forced my sister Soppy to draw my first fan art. I lub it*

Another day, a very smiley pretty girl asked, "Are you still using this Swiss ball?"

Avoiding eye contact, I emitted an unfriendly, "No."

No way was I going to nurture a new friendship.

"Los Angeles is known as one of the friendliest cities," said no one ever. I think I made my contribution.

I know I sound so mean. But trust me when I say I'm usually very social and have a habit of getting carried away with enjoying conversations with strangers and hanging out with friends much longer than intended. I had to be extremely isolated during the competition in order to stay focused. Also as a recovering hardcore people pleaser, it was best to avoid situations altogether that might suck me in.

# Chapter 6

# "I LIKE YOU"

> **For at the proper time we will reap a harvest if we do not give up.**
>
> **—Galatians 6:9**

"Why is it so hard for people to stay committed?" I asked.

"Because people's feelings change so often," My mom responded.

Remember how excited I was to embark on this contest? How competitive I felt with the previous year's tender-faced winner? Two weeks into the competition I forgot all about it. Not that the thought of quitting ever crossed my mind (very odd but thank God). It was just the day-to-day feelings changing on a whim, which messed with my head—Positive one moment! Negative the next. Fired up one day! Discouraged the next. Am I a psycho? Maybe! Maybe not.

But this time, I refused to let a feeling control my actions. I refused to be the fool who seeks short-term pleasures over long-term treasures! Speaking of fools . . .

Once upon a time, I dated a very successful older man who was very committed to his work, health, and family. He was everything I thought I wanted to be. (There's nothing weird about being attracted to a man because I want to be like him, right?) On the second date, I was so infatuated (and maybe drunk) that I proposed to him on two knees. Don't drink and drive or do dumb sheeit. #preventregret

On the third date, I snapped out of my drooling. He didn't want to be monogamous. Let's visit the scene where I redeemed myself:

**EXT. FANCY ITALIAN RESTAURANT - NIGHT**

FOOL (douchey, confident)

Monogamy is not natural. We're
animals. That's why most marriages
fail.


NINA

Actually, some animals commit to one
partner for life: eagles, wolves,
penguins, beavers, swans, even my
favorite insect: dung beetles . . .


FOOL

Well, not me. I need three girl-
friends with the freedom to sleep
with other women if I feel like it.


NINA looks right in his eyes. The fugger is
fuggin serious.

NINA

(in a calm voice, a tad New Jersey
mobster, like in "*The Sopranos*")

You wanna hump any woman you feel
like humping. Like a dumb squirrel,
huh. Do you also shit on anything you

feel like shitting on? Punch any asshole you feel like punching? Quit anything you feel like quitting?

FOOL is getting scared by the vascularity of her forehead. #foreheadgainz

                    NINA

What if committing to only one person gave you the most profound love you will ever experience? What if your 3 fake girlfriends and your million flings paled in comparison to the magnitude of being with this one person who really knew you, really laughed when you laughed, really hurt when you hurt, really fought in the trenches with you, really held you and really kissed you like no one else ever could AND you treasured her with equal in-tensity, depth, fortitude and loyalty?

FOOL

I was deeply in love with my previous
group of 3 girl-friends.


NINA

You know what, I wipe my ass with your
love.


She PLUNGES the steak knife into his fuggin
nuts.

And the world lived happily ever after.

---

Excuse me, based on a true story means some of it actually happened. The moral of the story is: it takes incredible self-discipline to not act according to what "feels good" in the moment and to choose to do what's best in the big picture, which is usually hard but necessary, right? I learned that from my favorite self-development author, Brian Tracy.

In talking to my mom about commitment and feelings, she sang me this cheesy but popular Korean song by Nam Jin and Jang Yun Jung called "I Like You." It goes like this:

73

I like you even when it's raining

I like you even when it' snowing

I like you even when it's windy

I like you even when it's sunny

I like you even when it's cloudy

. . . I like it all

This is how I had to be—consistent.

Remember my on-again, off-again relationship with eating healthy (and bingeing)? Going to college? Exercising? For me, I was used to doing things only when I felt like doing them. But because I wanted to win so badly, I automatically followed a long list of must-dos. Self-discipline is doing that you gotta do, when you gotta do it, no matter how you feel. UGH, I KNOW! I don't like hearing it either. I FEEL YOU, MANG!!!

Don't beat yourself up though. As humans, we all have this duality, according to Rick Warren, best-selling author of "Purpose Driven Life." In one of his talks, he acted out our mental struggle, "'I wanna do the right thing, but I don't. And I don't wanna do the wrong thing, but I do.' And that is the story of you. And it is the story of me." We all have this battle within us. But let's keep trying. The reward for self-discipline is greatness.

Some days I began lifting weights at 3pm, 7pm, or even midnight. But I never skipped a workout, even though most days I did not feel like exercising. Even pro bodybuilders don't always feel like working out. My negative thoughts and whining would pass and reoccur, and they SUCKED. But in the end, all that mattered was: did I get it done. And if I did, it was a win.

I worked out hard when I wanted to take it easy. I worked out when I would rather lie in bed. I stretched before and after my morning workout, and again, before and after my second workout.

Everything I did each day was centered around winning. For example, I prioritized sleep. I spent almost nine hours every day sleeping in order to lower my stress and maintain my energy without depending on caffeine or pre-workout drinks. If I needed to wake up at 11am to get a complete good night's rest, I did it. Even if it meant getting fired from one of my jobs.

Sometimes I would only go to work for my aunt for two hours and leave without explaining why. But I still got everything done—answering phones, replying to messages, and doing other tasks to make sure her vacation rentals ran smoothly and in accordance with Airbnb rules. She was incredibly generous to her favorite niece (wink). I usually left very abruptly when she was in the middle of something. I knew if I did not leave, I would get caught up in the drama of a family business, and I would risk losing precious time and energy for weightlifting.

What else was I doing to prioritize the competition? Very involved grocery shopping every few days; daily washing, precise measuring, and cooking food; daily cleaning a dozen food containers, blender, pots, pans, knives, peelers, etc.; and daily hand-washing the corsets. I had to research bodybuilding tips, watch and re-watch videos of perfectly executed exercises I had never done before, download audiobooks, and shop for anything to further challenge my workouts or lean me out.

I did not hang out with friends outside of the gym or work. Sometimes I called Muppet to whine, and he would always tell me that I could do it. But no long phone calls, no TV or movies, very little social media. I didn't miss social life, I welcomed the solitude to focus.

Do you REALLY wanna know to what extent I focused?

I abstained from the pleasures of the flesh. Manny Paquiao, one of the greatest boxers of all time, would stay chaste for 21 days before a fight. His trainer, Freddie Roach, warned, "Sex lowers your testosterone."[4] So I outdid Manny by more than three times that, because obviously, I'm more than three times the beast he is! I guess I had an advantage since no steaming hot tantalizer was knocking on my door, but that's irrelevant! I avoided dating apps and other temptations that would threaten my focus. I seriously considered every effin' detail that could possibly give me an edge. Kept my eye on the prize.

Whenever we undertake a big goal, we gotta expect to be tested by temptations and obstacles. If we stay the course till the end, we develop more resilience, thicker roots in our character. We witness first-hand that anything is truly possible. And we are the brave few living true to our heart.

# Chapter 7

# MACHINE MODE

> I hated training, but I told myself:
> Suffer now and live the life of a champion.
>
> —Muhammad Ali

It was the halfway point.

After waking up, it was time to take my progress pic in a bikini.

I was sure I'd see the outline of a six-pack.

No effin' way . . .

NOTHING.

*It's already halfway over. If I keep going at this rate, I'll lose.*

I'd been doing beginner level ab workouts for five, maximum ten minutes at a time, one to four times a week. So what did I expect? I had trusted that Beanstalk gave me all the exercises necessary to get the exact body I'd told her I wanted.

Panicking, I emailed her: "I just want to make sure the FOCUS is on getting a popping six-pack and rounded shoulders/biceps . . . The girl that won last year did not seem super lean in the legs, but her abs and shoulders looked huge."

Beanstalk advised me not to compare myself to the woman who won last year. I knew I didn't have to look exactly like Miss Librarian. But I felt very strongly about getting a six pack. I saw it as the badge of a bodybuilder and I assumed that it would impress the judges.

I remembered that Beanstalk had won bikini competitions where a six-pack was not required, so I felt a bit uneasy. She gave me one extra ab exercise to appease me and reassured me that I would be OK.

NO. I knew it would take a lot more work than that.

I figured I should never leave it all up to someone else, even if they knew a lot more than I did. I took it upon myself to get my own six-pack.

Around this time, I was listening to the audiobook version of Arnold Schwarzenegger's 2012 memoir, *Total Recall: My Unbelievably True Life Story*. In it, he explained that his calves were his weak point. Despite training them three times a week, as he did the rest of his body, they were not growing as well as his other impressive muscles. And he'd always assumed he'd been doing his very best and that no one could outdo his calf training: 300-pound calf raises, three times each week. That is, until he saw his childhood idol Reg Park do 1,000-pound calf raises, DAILY.

As Schwarzenegger wrote in his book:

> Stunned, "This is what I need to do. I have to train my calves totally differently and not give them even a chance of not growing." . . . I made a point of cutting off all my sweatpants at the knees . . . I made sure that my calves were exposed so everyone could see. I was relentless and did fifteen sets, sometimes twenty sets, of calf raises every single day. (p.94)

Now I was stunned: "OMG, this is what I need to do for my abs—except the part about cutting off my clothes for everyone to see!"

With only six weeks left, I decided to go hard, heavy, and a lot on my abs. Last time I was slim, I had no abs. I knew if I didn't push my abs, they would choose to stay comfortable and invisible.

I began scouring YouTube for fitness guys with blocky 3-D abs. I paid no attention to fitness models with light, pretty six-packs. Gimme that thick, that segmented, that chunky stuff! I tried everything they suggested, taking notes on which exercises made a difference in the appearance of my abs on the day after I did the particular exercise, or which burned the most during the exercise.

I made up a routine of the hardest ones and tossed the rest. (Someone even thanked me for my ab workouts, which helped them create their poppin' six pack, too. Go to my website www.ninanam.com and click on my YouTube channel to try it out!) I knew if it felt real effin' hard, I would get results. I gambled that an hour of intense ab work, six days a week, should do it. I added on abs to the end of my weight sessions, now I was stuck in the gym for three hours (plus that one-hour of death cardio in the morning).

Overtraining is subjective. My grandma doing 30 squats is overtraining. Me doing 300 is not. I knew hitting the same muscles six times a week went against what most trainers believed, but I trusted Arnold and I didn't have much time to play it safe. Go big or go home.

Plus, according to Mike Tyson's Wikipedia page, Mike's routine included 2,500 sit-ups with a 20-pound plate, so I thought, *OK, I'm not overtraining that much.*

Sometimes I had 5-pound ankle weights strapped onto each ankle when I was working out. Later I doubled the ankle weights. I tried stability balls, medicine balls, dumbbells, and a decline bench to make the ab exercises harder.

I'd do the heaviest, most intense moves first, then modify if I couldn't continue; for example: hanging leg lifts with ankle weights, first doing them with straight legs; then with bent knees. I'd get on the vertical chair, first with straight legs and later with bent knees. My goal was to keep the tension going, burning it out, never resting too long. I did full, controlled movements, not allowing momentum or cheating. I made sure to do several exercises developing the upper abs, the lower abs, and the obliques. Each exercise consisted of about 5 sets of 30 reps (a total of more than 600 ab moves).

I often reminded myself: "People who win these things usually are the ones who suffer the most."

If I did things I didn't want to do and that I doubted others would do, I figured I was closer to winning. You think I wanted to do an hour of abs on top of an already punishing workout? No way. But I had to take that chance, make that bet on winning.

A few days after I started implementing my genius idea to do an extra hour of ab exercises, this happened, as recorded in a message to Beanstalk: *I'm really sick :( ... I still worked out hard today but I feel wiped out.*

I woke up with a lot of phlegm in my throat. "NO! This is hard enough, getting sick is stupid! This shouldn't happen to people who sleep eight hours with one-hour naps mid-day!"

I later learned that many people during the transformation contest got sick because it is very taxing on the body. Too much too fast.

Hoping to get over the cold in a few days I overdosed on vitamin C, drank fresh ginger tea, and stayed in bed wrapped in blankets for as long as possible. Unfortunately, the intense thick phlegm lasted a week, and the coughing lingered for another week, despite mustering up all the positive thoughts I could.

On these mornings I woke up terrified.

Phlegmy, zero energy, slowly emerging out of bed like a zombie that had been shot in the face ten times but somehow kept moving forward—I went through the motions, and somehow the phlegm didn't choke me during the cardio death hour in the morning. I'd return home to lie in bed like a delicate corpse.

Before I knew it, it was the afternoon and time to go lift weights. Zero energy again. My shoulders felt like they were rounded forward and my chest sunken in. *How the heck am I gonna lift heavy today? What if I can't do my best?* I could not let that happen.

I wasn't afraid of losing the competition. I was afraid that my best efforts would not be enough. It was a deeply subconscious fear: if I am weak, then I am a loser and I am a nobody. It sounds ridiculous, right? But according to my favorite motivational author Louise L. Hay and Tony Robbins, everyone's underlying negative thought is the feeling of not being good enough.

Eating and training like that made me feel extra sensitive and perhaps more fearful, anxious than normal. I desperately wanted to give it my all, but I was afraid I couldn't give it my all. It's similar to the feeling you get in a nightmare—you desperately want to scream bloody murder, but you can barely make a sound and that scares you even more.

I would park my car in front of the gym and pray for help: "God, help me today, I don't know how I'm gonna do this, but help me if you want me to do it."

I would go inside the gym's bathroom and pray again: "God, I'm scared, just get me through this workout." Then I would just stand on that treadmill, frozen.

Hesitating and overthinking only delayed me from eating my next meal and meant being in the gym longer, so I had to stop my whining and just do it. Resisting, dreading how much I didn't want to work out prolonged the inevitable. I had to stop myself from wasting energy and quickly switch my focus to a simple task: Just put my feet on the damn treadmill and hit "START" as fast as possible. Then the rest would take care of itself.

I learned that it's OK not to have a noble motivation. Some days all I could say was "God, help me!" or "Let's just friggin' get this sheeit over with ASAP."

The day I was the sickest, I ended up lifting even heavier than the previous week. I increased by 2.5 and even 5 pounds on some exercises! That may not sound like a lot, but it was a big improvement, heck it was a miracle—not just because I was really sick, but I'd also cut calories.

I'd assumed I would lift the same as the previous week at best, but most likely less. I guess I doubted and feared a lot, before I even tried. Maybe I had no clue what I was capable of.

What happened was HYPER FOCUS.

Even on these days when I whined like hell, I could change my state of mind by focusing on the next tiniest step. I tried to stay focused on the immediate moment. Highly present. I would first focus on counting. I would focus on making that rep a perfect complete contraction, really feeling every bit of those muscle fibers. I would focus on exhaling when lifting/moving up; inhaling when releasing/moving down.

In that very moment of lifting, I find myself not having much thoughts, like a meditation where you might get a random thought here and there, but mostly you're too engaged in the process of counting and breathing correctly. Focusing that intensely made the overwhelm, whining, fear, and worrying disappear during that time. And then I could enter "machine mode," coined by Arnold. It's when you are giving it all you've got and nothing can hold you back now.

By placing one brick down perfectly, eventually I would have that perfect wall. Focus on just eating that one meal perfectly. A win! Focus on just placing that one foot on the Stairmaster perfectly. A win! Focus on just lifting that one rep perfectly. A win! I would try to focus on the burn, telling myself that the muscle was growing, telling myself that it was making a difference. The last few reps had to feel hard, like it was difficult to maintain perfect form. I would write down how much weight was my max and try to beat it the next time. Every day had to feel challenging; I tried to increase weight or increase speed whenever safely possible. Some days were the same as before, other days were not as good. But as long as I pushed myself, I checked it off as done.

One morning I had three sprints left, on an incline! I literally had to take it one second at a time, like this:

Only one minute of this crazy-ass sprint, and you get a mini-break. Don't think, just hit "START." GO! Come on, pick up those legs. Pick it up, PICK IT UP! That's it, you got the pacing just right. Pshh—I can totally do a minute of this! Maybe I'll even increase the speed for the next round. Alright, 45 seconds left, that's like 30 seconds! It's like already halfway over! Haha, good, good, good. Aw yeah, I can do this, easy. Uh-oh, my legs feel a little heavy now. Move your arms with more force, that'll pick up those legs! Ugh, it's not working as well as I thought. GET THEM LEGS UP!!! Thirty-five seconds left?! Sheeit! HUSH! It takes you longer to walk from your parking lot to your apartment, THIS IS NOTHING! It'll be over before you know it. NOO, still 28 SECONDS LEFT? It's only halfway over, and all that time that just passed must be repeated again! STOP THINKING LIKE

THAT! Come on, COME ON. Breathe, BREATHE. Use your arms, PUMP YOUR ARMS, be a machine. MACHINE. Twenty seconds. MACHINE! Tighten your abs. Belly button towards the spine. OMG, I want to stop. Friggin-a, how the hell am I gonna do this two more times? Don't even think about that now! Only 15 SECONDS LEFT! COME ON! YOU CAN DO IT, you're almost done, get it DONE. So close to 10 seconds . . . FINALLY, TEN SECONDS!! Almost done, almost done, almost done, finish it, finish it! Five more seconds, 4, 3, breathe, 2, 1—JUMP OFF!!!

FRIGGIN-A! WHAT THE HELL? OH MY GOD why is this one-minute break so much faster than that one-minute sprint? I can't believe I have to sprint again in 5 more seconds! AHHHHHHHHHHHHHHHHHHHHHHHHHHHH

[And repeat.]


Despite my fragile state, Beanstalk pulled the lever even more, cautioning, "This next phase will suck the most, and you'll be praying it's over." I know it sounds like a movie line, but I did not make this sheeit up!

*Chapter 8*

# THE ONE THING

I completely relate to JK Rowling when she said to Oprah in an interview in 2010:

> You've got to believe . . . I was not the world's most secure person. In fact, I was someone with not much self-belief at all. And yet, in this one thing in my life, I believed. That was the one thing in my life: I felt I can tell a story.

My one thing in my life: I can endure physical discomfort. That reads odd and maybe I'll regret writing this later and maybe it's not even my one thing, but I knew I had the ability to put up with pain a little longer than most people. I noticed it in work-out classes I'd participated in before the competition—I was always driven to finish what we were asked to do, and I never stopped to whine or complain (I swear the only time I've really grouched about working out was in this contest).

During this competition, my faith grew exponentially. I did not have complete trust in myself from the beginning. Every step I completed, I earned more trust in myself, built faith in myself. I wasn't passively wishing or hoping. It was an active, repetitive, fierce faith, a strong belief that things were going to happen in my favor. As I saw myself getting leaner, as my coach was impressed week by week, as I continued to eat perfectly, as my abs got stronger, as I checked off another task off the list—I grew more conviction. Despite feeling scared and exhausted most of the time, deep inside, I knew I had a chance at winning the whole time because of the massive effort I was putting in.

I'm friggin' lucky I felt so confident upon looking at the previous winner. That was my impetus for believing I could win. It immediately gave me confidence, and I decided to compete right then and there. "IF SHE CAN DO IT, I CAN DO IT." I can really win this thing—and remember, I came to this certainty when I was browsing the internet the day after one of my not uncommon, depressing binges.

Although I was struggling with my own self-esteem, I was not intimidated by her after-pic. I focused on her before-pic—her face looked even meeker than mine—and I felt encouraged by our similar starting points. I could push as hard or harder than she did, and get just as great of a transformation or better. And I was determined to see it play out.

Keeping that faith alive required research. From listening to audiobooks about my idols who turned their lives around, their success gave me the proof that it could be mine too. Also, I read several books on some of the "belief" practices they did to succeed, like affirmations and visualizations. I heard about visualization before, but I learned about how it could be a super power if practiced in a certain way.

For example, Tony Robbins helped Andre Agassi go from being 32nd in men's tennis to number one in six months' time, using visualization. Tony got Agassi to envision his perfect swing, over and over again, *feeling it vividly*. Agassi wasn't thinking about the swing, he didn't get caught up on the details or the mechanics of how to do it—he just focused on the *feelings* that came with doing that perfect swing.

You don't even have to be good at visualization for it to work.

Lanny Basham, Olympic gold medalist in rifle shooting, explained visualization in a similar way in his 1988 memoir, *With Winning in Mind*: "Many players are concerned that they cannot seem to get a sharp picture and do not really SEE clearly when they try to visualize . . . it is not what you SEE that is important but what you FEEL" (p. 35).

Lanny Basham wanted to set the national record for rifle shooting at a perfect score, 400, but he'd never fired a 400, not even during practice. So, for several times a day for two months, he rehearsed in his mind while reinforcing the feelings he wanted, like this:

> I vividly rehearsed shooting the first 100, then another and another. I visualized each of the last ten shots building toward the record. I rehearsed what I knew would happen at that point: I would realize that I was above the record. Next, I rehearsed hearing a voice say, "That's OK, I do this all the time." Then I imagined shooting the final ten easily and saying to myself, "Another 400, that's just like me." (p. 67)

And that was exactly how it happened when he set the national record.

This is how my visualization played out: I tried visualizing hundred dollar bills. But I felt nothing. I tried visualizing Bodybuilding.com surprising me at my gym to announce that I won. But it still didn't feel real, like I was forcing myself to feel excited about it. I got frustrated with what exactly I should imagine. It was hard, mang!

So, instead of thinking of the outcome (money or surprise visit), I visualized what I needed to win. Since I was working on my six-pack, I would imagine that. But I had no idea how it would look on me. I knew I wanted it to be round and feminine, not skinny or wide. But even that visualizing felt distant, too cerebral, kinda abstract.

So I used touch to help me imagine. I am a very tactile person, so I placed my hand on my abs during exercises to feel them contract. And I told myself: *Ah yeah, there it is. That's them thickening and growing with every movement just like that.* I felt for where the exact dividers were, feeling them pop as I crunched my abs. This reinforced my belief that every time I did a hard move, my ab muscles were actually growing, and that my six-pack was emerging.

On a normal day without a severe diet, I can do a 20-minute steady-state jog at a 1.0% incline, no problem. But in the final weeks of the competition, working out four hours a day with a corset on as well as a thick coating of Sweet Sweat, a double wrapping of Saran Wrap, and a sweat-inducing beanie, I was feebly gasping for air at a 6.0 pace (that's like a solid jog, a 10 minute mile, nothing super loco). I had to engage my brain on an audiobook; otherwise I would have kept looking at the clock every thirty seconds, freaking out that I had a long way to go.

Listening to autobiographies and self-help books uplifted and inspired me, or at least, distracted me long enough to stop myself from whining. I was amazed by Lucille Ball's focus and fierceness as a businesswoman and actress. "I'm not funny. What I am is brave." I loved hearing how Tony Robbins grew up so poor. And my heart just expanded whenever Louise L. Hay declared affirmations so powerfully yet so sensitively and lovingly. And she was able to dramatically transform her life after 40! I wanted to hear from people who'd overcome great suffering and reached great success. I wanted to learn from legends who changed the world.

I wanted a different life, and I knew that would require a different mind. My own whining and negative thoughts annoyed me during these secluded three months. Audiobooks were my favorite way to step away from my automatic thought patterns and just brainwash myself with positivity and hope. I wanted to be a sponge to anything that would lead me to an amazing life. I didn't want that old unfulfilling one.

In the first half of the competition, I thought I was pursuing an amazing body and money, chasing a mirage of happiness.

Later, the money and the bod started to sound not worth it for all the torture. I could get a hot bod and make my own money without killing myself like this, by taking my time instead of rushing in "12 weeks." But I kept grinding anyway. I'd already invested so much time and money, and something kept pulling me to finish.

And as the days kept passing, I realized what I did want out of this competition: to be able to say, "I gave it my all." That sounded really worth it, especially because this was the hardest thing I had ever done. I wanted the right to own that for myself. Exactly what I wanted to be able to say was: *I gave it my all and I have no regrets; there was nothing more I could've done.* Notice, this never mentions winning, the body, or the money. I eventually stopped thirsting for the money and the bod.

Looking back now, I can see what I deeply wanted more than anything else in the world was to be proud of myself for once. I wanted to love who I was. No, I think it's even more simple, more immediate than that . . .

I just wanted to like myself.

This transformation contest was not about beating everyone else and winning. It was about keeping a promise to myself, which was unfortunately rare. And, by taking steps every day towards that promise (i.e., finishing this contest to the best of my ability), I actually liked myself more. That is faster and more effective than saying, "I love you," or "You're beautiful," in the mirror a dozen times. Taking steps toward my big goal increased my self esteem, big time.

In the final most difficult month, I was surprised by a very intense feeling that came to the surface seemingly out of nowhere. During one of my running bouts in the morning, I was starting to feel emotional; maybe it was the music I was listening to. I remembered that familiar old feeling—like when that girl got picked on by the picked-on boy; like when that girl got rocks thrown at her head by the cool kids. I got crazy angry on that treadmill, two parts of me battling it out:

**Voice X**: You are still a loser.

**Voice Y**: No, I'm not a loser anymore.

**Voice X**: Look at how lame your life is. You don't have your shit together! You are still a loser!

**Voice Y**: NO, I AM NOT A LOSER.

**Voice X**: Then prove it. Prove you're never going to be a loser anymore. This is your chance to stop being a loser and do something different for once. Right here, right now.

**Voice Y**: I AM NOT A LOSER! I AM A FIGHTER! I AM A FIGHTER AND I DON'T EFFIN' CARE IF MY LEGS FALL OFF RIGHT NOW!

That really drove me to the edge. I was subconsciously trying to smash the old tapes that had been running my life. I couldn't overeat junkfood or overuse social media or goof around with friends to avoid this negative voice. I faced it head-on, and it was intense. But to my surprise, it lasted less than a few minutes.

I used to re-read Lance Armstrong's quote for comfort: 'Pain is temporary. It may last a minute or an hour or a day or even a year. But, eventually it will subside and something else will take its place. If I quit, however, it will last forever . . . I dare you to take a little pain. I dare you . . . At the end of pain is success."

Psychologist Martin Seligman, found that about two-thirds of the "dogs, rats, mice and even cockroaches that experienced mildly painful shock over which they had no control would eventually just accept it, with no attempt to escape." [5] His studies with people also showed that most don't try to figure out how to stop the incessant noise, and they become passive. That is learned helplessness. However, "about a third of the animals and people who experience inescapable shocks or noise never become helpless." This is because of optimism. "People who don't give up have a habit of interpreting setbacks as temporary, local, and changeable. ('It's going away quickly; it's just this one situation and I can do something about it.')" 6

Tony Robbins said in a seminar, "Pessimists are much more realistic, they are much more accurate . . . optimists always see themselves as doing better than they really did . . . so they keep doing it, because they have the illusion they did well . . . and because of that optimism, they did it more often, and so optimists succeed at a four- to five-fold . . . result ultimately beyond anything that a pessimist will do."7

I like to think of myself as in that special third of animals and people that never give up. I love trying things that may benefit me greatly, even if nothing comes of it, but at least I tried. I really expected God to give me something great out of this experience, as selfish as that may sound. And that hope made me an optimist and made me willing to endure pain.

# Chapter 9

# GRATEFUL BEAST

> **The single greatest thing you can do to change your life today would be to start being grateful for what you have right now.**
>
> **—Oprah**

I was good at protecting my mind from outside influences, following the diet and exercise. The real challenge, the one I keep returning to is managing my own mind.

Even with all my reading and brainwashing, my negative thoughts still got to me. I wish I could say that before I opened my eyes every morning, I acknowledged what I was grateful for, prayed for others, did powerful visualization exercises, and then leaped out of bed like a happy beast! Instead, I woke most mornings freaked out by the sound of my alarm and whimpering. I crawled out of bed like a patient who had been hit by a bus last night. Thank goodness for glutamine and BCAAs; at least I never felt painfully sore.

After just a week into the competition I wrote an email to Beanstalk: *DAMN you can barely [see any] difference . . . Freakin' need . . . to get bigger.*

You see, I'm very much a VIP: Very Impatient Person. What I needed to acknowledge was that invisible changes happen first inside, and visible changes appear later outside. And an invisible change had already started to twinkle and sparkle into life—it happened that moment I saw Ms. Librarian's face and knew I could win.

Remember how I said enduring physical pain was my one thing? With that said, I hope you trust that I'm not one to complain or whine easily. Keep that in mind when reading these other messages I wrote to Beanstalk:

> *Goddam most days I wanna lay down all day and I get scared when I wake up!*

> *Man this shit really tests your mind so much. Cried twice yesterday.*

> *Why do I feel like a melted candle today? I slept less than ideal but took a long nap. Now I'm scared shitless about tonight's workout. I always get so worried that I won't be able to give it my all. I've been pretty strong all week and now I feel so weak,*

*it's exhausting to even walk from my car to my apt.
All I did was lay down today . . . sheeeeeeit*

No matter how I felt though, I always pushed myself. I even tested two different twenty-pound weighted vests when running and cycling, because—why not? I was dead anyway, might as well burn a few more calories . . . But I returned them soon after I noticed myself moving slower due to the added weight; it would be better to lean out my legs by running and cycling faster—or try to at least!

At one point I wrote Beanstalk the following: *had to stop half my workout to nap and resume later, also held onto treadmill the entire time :c* Both my arms were tightly wrapped around the control panel of the treadmill, with my chest leaning on it (hugging it would be an understatement). I literally had my legs running behind me. Don't do it! As an Asian, I didn't want to add onto the stereotype that we are unathletic. . . at least we got Bruce Lee. (Unfortunately, my mom contributes to the other stereotype that Asians are bad drivers. She still drives around town 10 miles below the speed limit.)

As uncool as it looked, I figured that if I didn't hold on for dear life, I might fly off the treadmill or, even worse, have to lower the speed. And I couldn't lower the speed, no way mang! I may not have burned as many calories with my arms not moving, but as long as my legs were in full-on running motion I convinced myself that it would make a difference in the appearance of my thighs, just by letting them jiggle and burn.

My excuse—and I think it's a good one—low carbs limited my logic and helped me forget the importance of safety first. I was getting weaker every week, with less food. I lost my period that final month.

I got to a point where the same fun pop songs weren't pushing me anymore; they became white noise. So I tried uplifting Christian music, but that made me lose my beast mode! (Sorry God!) That's when I discovered extreme music: dubstep. It sounds like robots dancing and screaming in outer space. It got me out of my head real quick and took me into a silly fantasy that actually worked. Fasted morning cardio was me in my imaginary action movie: I was the star, a badass robot cop running, jumping into my hot futuristic police car to catch the bad guys. It made me smile and helped the time pass. Unusual thoughts are normal at this stage.

Then the time came when even dubstep wasn't enough to get me through. I begged Muppet to work out with me a few times in the final weeks to prevent me from getting so scared. He even laughed because I couldn't explain what I was afraid of, why I needed someone to be by my side so badly. "No, I'm not in love with you."

"No, I wasn't afraid of falling or getting hurt." "No, I don't need you to motivate me."

Like I mentioned earlier, I was deeply afraid of not being good enough, of disappointing myself. But at the time, I didn't know how to put it in words and didn't understand why I suddenly needed someone next to me. I'm not a needy person by any means, but I was willing to pay him to go to the gym with me. Thank God Muppet generously donated his time to babysit me.

To put me at ease, he copied all of my moves and cracked his stupid jokes. I didn't ask him to pay attention to my execution, but he couldn't help it because he used to be a trainer. One time, we were doing shoulder raises with dumbbells. Muppet stopped me and firmly suggested instead of using swinging with momentum, I should use lesser weight with proper form. Sheeit, I wasn't focusing.

"I got this," I ungratefully snapped.

*I'm not gonna lower my weight, these ten pounds are pathetic enough* . . . I tried to go slower with control, I couldn't lift it. I quickly dropped the ten pounders and grabbed the 8-pounders. Muppet was probably patting himself on the back for that one.

My weights kept getting lighter in the final weeks. Apparently, all bodybuilders, as they reach their deadline, cannot lift as much as they did off-season due to their restricted diets necessary for achieving below-survivable body fat percentage.

After only fifteen reps I felt so winded, like it would be wise to stop exercising for a few months (which is what I did after the competition ended, oh sheeit, this girl don't sugarcoat nuffin'). My heart was beating meekly. My chest felt concaved again. And it was just the beginning of our three-hour workout.

Because Muppet used to do hardcore Muay Thai training, he yelled out the hardest ab workouts he could think of on the fly, and I had no choice but to do whatever he said. I told him to have no mercy.

One time, he made me stand with my hands clasped in front of my chest. He told me to do whatever it took to stay in that exact position and he would try to push my hands around. He pushed my hands down, up, to the side. As hard as I tried, my hands moved all over the place.

For shits and giggles, he picked me up by my clasped hands and threw my body a few feet away. He burst out laughing. I alternated between meek laughing and dying, but I never gave up and I kept crawling back for more, didn't I? You poophead!

I wrote to Beanstalk: *I hate wondering if it's my mind being weak or if I'm genuinely spent.* Yes, my emails were getting repetitive (and probably annoying to Beanstalk). But, these thoughts plagued me in the final weeks: "Am I truly physically exhausted or am I weak-minded?" If I was truly strong, I wouldn't feel so exhausted, right?

What I was really asking was: "Am I truly doing my best . . . am I more than good enough?" If I wasn't, I felt tremendous guilt. It was like a little grey cloud that I carried around. Remember, I explained that as the competition continued, the money and the bod were no longer my driving force. What I wanted out of the competition was to be able to say, "I gave it my all and I have no regrets; there was nothing else I could've done." This was so important to me, yet I had no way of measuring what my best was . . . I found myself constantly haunted by the possibility I could've pushed a little harder, done a little more.

Beanstalk told me that I was supposed to feel wiped out. Plus, I was doing an additional hour of exercise from what she had personally gone through herself and had recommended for me. Plus, I always wore my excessive sweating contraptions. But I still feared I was not good enough, that I maybe possessed a weak mind like a loser.

107

I needed something more powerful to bring me peace and focus—and that's where gratefulness came in.

When you think of what you're grateful for, you naturally think positive thoughts. The more positive your thoughts, the less space for negative thoughts. My username for the contest was "GRATEFULBEAST." I created this username not only to remind myself to be grateful but also with the hope that when I won, people would see it and also remember to be grateful beasts.

Gratitude, saying what I was grateful for—that's something I wanted to make a habit. At first, I did it because I heard the more you are thankful for what you currently have, the more you will receive to be thankful for in the future. But after trying it, I loved how it made me more calm, more in touch with my heart and just happier immediately.

After about a month, I really liked my physical changes, they were promising—until one day Beanstalk pointed out my thighs required extra running on the treadmill. Apparently, it was a common "problem" area for female bodybuilders. While I'd never seen them as a "problem" before, after Beanstalk's comment, I started to see their flaws and stewed unkind, ungrateful thoughts towards them.

After every tormenting running session, I would check the next day if they were getting any leaner. Disappointed in seeing such slow progress, I'd berate myself, "Beanstalk had lean thighs, but you don't have a single line showing. At this rate, you'll just have corn-dog thighs and look like you didn't try at all."

Weeks later, I was stretching after a hard leg workout. As I bent over my left leg to stretch the hamstring, I looked down and suddenly saw a skinny thigh. I remembered how "thick" it was just a month ago, and now it was just a portion of what it used to be.

I burst into tears. I felt sad for it. It was disappearing this whole time, doing what I punished it to do, showing up whenever I needed it to give me 100%. It never gave me any trouble. How mean I had been to that shrinking leg!

I leaned over that leg and hugged it, saying, "Thank you, Leg, you are so strong and you did so much for me today." I started to realize how my legs never got injured, sprained, or strained. Not even a cramp! My legs were actually effin' amazing!

Ever since then I would remember to say thank you to a specific body part during stretching. I would whisper to that body part, "Thank you, Arm, for working hard for me today." It's like those studies by Dr. Singh about how plants react favorably to classical music and Dr. Emoto's studies on how water molecules change into beautiful shapes upon hearing loving words.

Feel grateful often. Feel great often.

# Chapter 10

# FATHERS

*Walk by faith not by sight.*

*—2 Corinthians 5:7*

I just finished an hour on the treadmill—a bunch of sprinting, jogging uphill, walking lunges, and squats.

Huffing and puffing still, I cooled down, walking slowly on the treadmill. I was relieved it was over but started to get angry, like this sheeit better be worth it. Looking up towards the ceiling, I aggressively prayed under my breath, "I know you see me putting in the work, God. You know I'm all in . . ."

Then I made Him an offer he couldn't refuse: "If you help me win, I will tell the whole world it was because of you."

I knew He would like that.

I needed to know that He was going to really help me. That He was in it to win it, too.

I wasn't sure that this prayer would work or if it was OK to pray to like that, but I felt that He heard me and I expected Him to really be there for me. And I didn't feel as alone. Knowing that He was watching over me, helped me hold on when the going got tougher.

God's presence in my workouts felt a lot like my dad's presence when he helped me win some small but significant things. For example, in seventh grade orchestra class I wanted to win a "challenge." The jerk that sat in front of me thought she was better than me, and I had to teach her a lesson.

The way a challenge worked was that our teacher would put us both in the storage room with the door closed. We would take turns playing the same piece, anonymously. Afterwards, the class would vote which sounded better. If mine sounded better, I would get her seat, and she would step down to take my old seat. If I lost, I would look like an idiot!

My dad spent a long time listening and watching me play the violin. I told you that I rarely practiced, but I didn't say I never practiced. I had to practice for important sheeit that mattered, like beating a girl I didn't like!

So my dad, with no experience playing the violin, told me to just vibrato the sheeit out of my violin and make a dramatic contrast between the quiet part and the loud part. He passionately encouraged me to keep wiggling my fingers, and I would, even though my fingertips hurt from aggressively rubbing them into strings to create that soft beautiful sound. If I had practiced regularly, they would have been properly calloused.

Because my dad was there in it with me, wanting me to do my best, I worked hard. I made sure to start out soft and then swell into strong loud strokes with my bow. He stayed with me until I felt confident that I could vibrato the whole piece to shreds and control the volume.

I was nervous, but I beat that girl fair and square.

Another time my dad helped me win was in my first speech contest in high school. I was painfully shy, so my parents suggested I try a speech contest, which sent me into a long crying tantrum. They pointed at the Korean newspaper that promised, "It will change your child's life."

*That's not gonna change my life, that's gonna end my life!*

They negotiated with me: Just do one contest and if you don't like it, you never have to do it again. That was the best deal I was going to get, so I agreed.

That Korean newspaper was right. It changed my life. It obliterated a roof that had kept me feeling small, giving me the opportunity to be heard and seen.

To help me prepare for the contest, my dad took me to the ocean late at night when no one was around. Shoes off, facing the moonlit water, he started shouting the alphabet, loud and proud. Then he encouraged me to do the same. Like a Lion to his baby lion.

The crashing of the black waves muted my meek, half-assed attempts. When I paused, he roared the next letter, hoping I would get more into it. But I felt unbearably awkward and embarrassed. Not even halfway into the alphabet, I gave up.

"I can't get louder," I told him.

"It's alright," he said calmly.

And we went home.

I felt so bad for letting him down and for not trying harder, even though he'd been so understanding and kind. But he's not the type that gives up.

Later he videotaped me practicing my speech, and when I watched myself for the first time, I was horrified at how boring and weak I appeared. After that we spent weeks experimenting with volume, enunciation, emphasis, pauses, and grand dramatic gestures, none of which came naturally to me. Overtime I learned to love being vocal, expressive, and sometimes over the top.

The day of the speech contest, my mom gave me the best pep talk: "No matter how much I want to poop your poop for you, I can't. You must poop your own poop."

That fired me up! I was gonna friggin' poop my own poop!

My knees wobbled the entire ten steps walking up to that podium. There were only two other speakers and around ten people in the small hotel conference room. I did everything as practiced and felt more and more confident as I kept going. Suddenly, I realized that one of the judges was sleeping! Annoyed, I slammed my fist on the podium, causing the mic to wobble, and I saw her eyes pop open. That sudden display of fist-slamming enthusiasm had nothing to do with my stance on whether or not cloning was ethical, but I won.

The gentle presence, support, and love I felt from God was just as real and encouraging as that of my real dad. I don't have any crazy stories like suddenly hearing His voice or lifting a hundred pounds more than usual. It was subtle.

God kept me sane. I prayed to Him more as time went on. The loneliness of working out alone, avoiding people and distractions, and not numbing out with food allowed me to get better acquainted with God. I went to church on and off since I was a kid, but this was the first time I really let Him into my heart.

I didn't have a ritual of praying on my knees upon waking or anything formal. I just talked to Him out loud or under my breath, whenever I needed Him.

Before I talked to Him, I usually closed my eyes. I would get quiet for a moment and just feel His presence within my heart. Once connected, my heart softened, my mind relaxed, and time slowed down.

One time I was lying on the gym floor, tears trickling, too exhausted to wipe them. I don't remember what workout I was doing, how I ended up there, or who saw me. All I remember is that my body was saying stop. Then I prayed within my heart, "God, if you want me to finish this workout, give me that second wind." I never got a holy burst of energy, but after laying there for a few minutes thinking about God, I got up to finish it.

Like my real dad, God was a trusted love right by my side. He really saw me. He knew my heart, and He knew all the effort I was putting in, more than anyone else would ever know. He was my faith. And my focus.

# Chapter 11

# EFFIN' FINISH IT ALREADY

> *If you are going through hell, keep going.*
>
> *—Winston Churchill*

Around the halfway point, my mom visited me. She is very observant. As she stood in the kitchen, she looked straight into my eyes and said, "You've already won."

I was caught off-guard.

She said, "Make this your number one priority. Don't talk on the phone, don't work too much, take off work the last two weeks before the deadline. Do everything to make this the most important thing."

I didn't even think to ask her to clarify what she meant by "You've already won." Like did she think I would literally win or that I had won in life in general by having some discipline for once?

In that moment all I felt was "She believes in me." And when you love your mom, that is powerful. The fire that was already inside of me intensified. I felt more determined and confident. Everyone deserves support and love like that.

Once I caught her looking at me sadly, and she quickly turned her head, mumbling, "You have lost so much weight, I can't even look at you." She always liked me chubby, yet she still supported me because she saw something special happening within me.

I've never suffered as much as my mom or my Halmunee . . .

My mom says she was well off compared to the other poor kids in her little village. But she was living with an alcoholic dad and alcoholic grandpa, both draining precious money. There was constant verbal and physical fighting—bowls of food thrown violently and shattering across the floor; a long, sharp garden hoe sledge-hammered into her dad's head. For 30 years, my mom often experienced dangerous food comas, bloody noses, extreme weakness, and other health problems she didn't know was caused by childhood-onset diabetes.

Upon immigrating to California, she had to confront racism. (I was like "Huh? People were still racist in the '80s?") Even though she looked classy, sophisticated, and beautiful, someone spit on her car, someone made her wait in the back of the line, another told her to go back to her country. She worked full-time while studying for several licenses and certifications as she raised four kids.

After decades with my father, they had a dramatic divorce. She went through bankruptcy. I remember one time, my mom confided, "If I had to die for you, I would do it. I could do it right now. With no hesitation." That freaked me out.

Halmunee, my grandma from my mom's side, survived two major wars and raised seven children in rural South Korea. She worked before sunrise in muddy, snake-and-mosquito-ridden rice fields without help from her alcoholic husband. She trekked far for fresh water and firewood for her family, she washed clothes in a stream, she sewed holey clothes by candlelight, *and* she cleaned the shitty wooden port-a-potty used by all 11 or so people (basically everything sucked, but that last part would destroy me). Her in-laws lived with her and treated her like a slave. I asked her why she didn't just friggin' run away from it all, and she sighed, "Because I was stupid."

Now her back is so bent that her head points towards the ground, and she can only stand upright with a cane. When I visited her years back, I was getting out of the taxi in front of her house, and she threw her cane aside and ran towards me the best she could, physically gnawing my shoulder, laughing, "I just want to eat you!"

Both are the most loving, passionate, disciplined women I've ever known.

Sometimes I'd think, "Oh no, one minute of high knees again!" Then quickly I'd command myself, "I'm gonna finish this effin' one minute; one minute is nothing! Mom and Grandma suffered so much. If they could suffer all that, I can suffer this tiny bit. This is nothing compared to what they've been through. You never suffered your whole selfish spoiled life. Arghhhh!!! I'm finishing this!" I would do that after what felt like endless sprints and lunges.

Many of my relatives sacrificed a lot and continue to work very hard. But like my mom said, "You don't succeed just because you work very hard. You can labor your whole life in the rice fields until you break your bones, but what do you have left?" It's important to work hard, but it's also important to have a purpose for the hard work.

So what about me—what was the purpose of exercising and eating like this?

The closer I got to the end of the competition, the smaller the meals became, the longer the workouts got in order to look beef-jerky lean—more cardio, more reps, and more nauseating asparagus to swallow. No fruits the final week. And those "smaller meals?" This was breakfast: a quarter-cup of cooked oatmeal, two tablespoons of chalky brown rice protein powder, and a cup of asparagus. Did this mean I could take it a little easier when I worked out? UH, NO! I still had to lift as heavy as possible despite feeling like that wimpy weak cartoon character from *Popeye*, what's her face? Olive Oyl!

The final three days were the best, though: 5 lb dumbbells and light resistance bands to keep muscles stimulated just enough but careful not to cause fluid buildup. And I ate only carbs and protein (no salt or asparagus). I drank significantly more water (1.5+ gallons) for a few days to trick my body into thinking there was an abundance of water. Then for the final three days I drank significantly less water with dandelion root to really dry out my body. I was chapped in every orifice.

I remember asking myself so many times, "What's the point of all this—just to look good and win against other masochists killing themselves? Is there a deeper reason I got into this weird superficial sport?" I knew the purpose would be revealed to me eventually. What helped me push forward is reading this verse in particular: "The pain that you have been feeling cannot compare to the joy that is coming" (Romans 8:18).

Towards the end, I made deep prayers for the strength to finish. I kept reminding myself that it was almost over. I wasn't thinking about the money or how hot I would look. I just wanted to get the effin' thing finished. I was craving to prove to myself that I finished something very hard, the hardest thing I'd ever done in my life. I came so far, I knew I was very close to having that intense gratification. I'd love to be able to say that. It sounded so worth it.

*The day before the day of my after-photos:* Muppet came over to do a test shoot using his nice camera. We were testing lighting and makeup. I hired a professional makeup artist and paid $200 just for the test shoot. I looked like a run-down prostitute with flat abs. Dehydrated, emaciated-ish, bad makeup, fake tan . . .

*One of the practice pics. Muppet always cracked me up no matter how down I got.*

I cried when I saw the practice pics. All my hard work had been in vain. My abs, face, skin, everything looked weird, nothing close to the badass image I'd been aiming for. I knew I'd lost. I felt so confused, so dumb. *I guess I still can't do anything right. I'm just an idiot living in my own bubble of hope. And on top of that, I'm friggin' ugly as hell.* With one negative thought came a flood of them.

Muppet, doing his best to crack me up and dry my tears, reassured me that he would make me look good. But I doubted it and held no expectations for the big day. He and my sister spent all night researching how to set up lights and then buying all kinds of lights and little gadgets to hold them in place.

*The day of my after-photos*: I took a brisk walk outdoors. I didn't need a treadmill for this easy cardio. It was the first time I "exercised" outside of the gym in a long time, and it was friggin' glorious. It felt like I was in that Disney movie when the Old Tree Lady starts singing to Pocahontas, "Listen with your heart, you will understand . . ." and the wind starts swirling her hair in slow motion with leaves and sparkly sheeit. My skin cells literally quivered feeling the ocean breeze a mile away, and my ear hairs tingled hearing the soft spring leaves rustling in the trees. I felt so happy and free. Finally, the friggin' day had come!

I did some light resistance band workout. I consumed a tiny bit of cream of wheat and protein powder. I drank half a cup of black coffee in hopes of pooping prior to the pictures . . . I didn't get lucky. I thought this was how marathon runners took a crap before a long race! At least you couldn't tell I was full of crap in the pics. Well, I wasn't eating much, semi-full of crap. Let that sizzle in your imagination as you look at my bikini pics.

I was nervous but quiet. I thought I looked better than on the previous day, but I wasn't sure. Maybe those carbs after the test shoot plumped me up a bit. I decided that I wasn't going to let my opinion of my body ruin my focus for the next few hours. There was nothing I could do but follow the rest of the remaining procedures Beanstalk had given me. At least I was doing my own makeup, and I wouldn't look like a cakey drag queen.

My sister Weemee had flown into LAX just to help me with this photoshoot. She helped me apply coconut oil all over my body. I ate a tablespoon of white rice with a teaspoon of agave. Then I started pumping up to create a fuller look. In the mirror I observed a tired skeleton lifting five-pound dumbbells. It was a creepy creature: 14% body fat. Bones and muscles that I'd never seen before.

I wasn't self-conscious wearing such a tiny cheap bikini in front of Muppet and the camera because my body just didn't feel real. I told myself I never wanted to look this skinny ever again. Hopefully I'd look better in the photos than what I was seeing. I refocused all of my attention to hitting all of the poses perfectly as practiced. That's all I had control over now.

My chest felt concaved as usual. As I continued pumping up, my heart felt weaker than ever. Twenty-five reps for every muscle: front raises, side lateral raises, overhead presses, upright rows, pushups-wide, pushups-narrow, tricep kickbacks, bicep curls, chest flies, ab crunches, leg raises, hip raises, bicycle crunches, jump squats, lunges, calf raises. I hoped I wouldn't have to do all that exhausting muscle-pumping over again.

I slipped on some nude high heels to jack up my calves. I didn't even ask if this was allowed, I just did it.

We worked first on the money shot: the front pose. I was certain this was the shot that Bodybuilding.com would use on their website, so it was the shot they would probably judge off of. I bet it was the deciding factor for the winner. So I wanted to spend the most energy on this pose, while my energy was at its highest.

For the side pose—pop the glutes, shoulders, calves. Lastly, the back pose—arch the low back so intensely to create a tiny waist—careful not to cramp up—breathe— made as many ugly faces as I wanted. Now stick out the butt and show off the biceps.

I had a lot more requirements for my front pose. First of all, Muppet directed me to smile. I thought I was smiling! He said I looked constipated. Yes, I was, but that's not the point. It was hard to genuinely smile while exhaling and tightening my abs, popping my shoulders up, softly placing my fingers on my hips, squeezing the life out of my thighs, and standing tall in high heels.

Weemee was hustling. She ran around tilting and moving around five different light bulbs to create nice shadows on my muscle definition—one above me, one on each side, and some next to the camera. She was also in charge of keeping my cheap, wobbly five-dollar full-length mirror upright, next to the camera for me to see that I was posing exactly how I wanted to.

After two hours of setting up and shooting, we had great side and back pictures, but no good front poses. My abs looked kinda flat in all of them. My little heart sank. Maybe I hadn't worked them out as hard as I'd thought. Maybe I was cocky for thinking I could get a six pack so fast.

Muppet was tired. Weemee was tired. No one had taken a break or done anything else. And I was getting shakier by the minute. I needed to eat, but I would allow myself one more tablespoon of white rice and a teaspoon of agave only if I absolutely had to pump up again as per coach's orders.

Muppet showed me the best front picture we'd gotten so far. Unacceptable. This was not going to be the picture I submitted after all this effin' work. Angry at myself, I impulsively shouted, "DO IT AGAIN."

Muppet and Weemee sighed. They were dealing with a maniac.

I grabbed the little container with my last premade tablespoon of white rice mixed with a teaspoon of agave, and inhaled the mini carbs to do their magic: make me pop.

*THIS IS THE SPRINT TO THE END. . . THIS IS IT.*

*RIGHT NOW!*

I jumped onto my back, on the carpet, ripping through 25 sit-ups, 25 leg lifts, 25 bicycles as fast as I could. I'm sure it looked like a sad attempt to work out. My body was shaking from lack of fuel, like a shivering Chihuahua. My shaking made me nervous, shooting up my adrenaline, making me even shakier, making me even angrier and more determined to power through. Everything I worked for was for this moment. It was an animalistic aggressive focus.

*MY SIX-PACK WILL POP, I WILL FORCE THEM TO COME OUT.*

I jumped up to do 25 jump squats, but I couldn't jump high. My legs were trembling, they couldn't handle it, but I made them do it. If I fell on my carpet, so what. I felt my heart meekly pounding.

*COME ON, THIS IS THE LAST TIME I'LL TORTURE YOU.*

Immediately I jumped into lunges. It was do-or-regret-forever. I forgot about pumping up my arms. It didn't matter. My strong points were going to be my overall leanness, six-pack, and thighs . . . I hoped.

I demanded out loud, "COME ON, LET'S GO, I'M READY."

I didn't want to be pushy to my favorite people, but we had no time. My abs were as full as they'd ever be, and my sister had a plane to catch.

Muppet and Weemee were really stressed out from all my pressure. They wanted so badly to make sure I would get the pics I needed. Weemee stubbed her toe running to adjust the light a little more and cursed out loud. Muppet was getting irritated by my impatience with him to hurry with the pictures. He was taking them, but either the lights weren't hitting me right or I wasn't smiling genuinely.

I was in fight-or-flight mode, actually fight mode; I totally looked uneasy and stressed. Someone said something funny amidst this tension, and I ended up laughing. Muppet snapped a shot.

"I think we got it," Muppet announced, and showed it to me on the camera.

It looked the best so far, but . . .

"Are you sure? Can we take a few more . . .?"

"No, that's it. It's not gonna get any better than this. Besides you look better here than in real life!"

What a poophead. But he was right, everything popped exactly how I wanted.

I got Weemee to LAX on time. I drove back home calmly, almost dreamlike, realizing, *It's finally over. What a friggin' relief.*

I thought about how much Weemee loved me for her to fly all the way out just to help me. I hadn't even paid for her ticket. I thought about how Muppet cared about me so much throughout the whole thing—French fry incident and all. I felt grateful for everyone, everything, and for the contest for changing my life.

I was so proud of myself for finishing. I wasn't used to finishing stuff. This was the hardest thing I'd ever done up to that point in my life. I really had no regrets. I did everything I said I would. I truly gave it my all. And that was the real prize.

Waiting for the light to change on Lincoln Boulevard, I sobbed like an Oscar award-winning actress in a tragic movie. I didn't care if I won. I'd already won. I'd really won.

# EPILOGUE

*The best prize of all is having finished what you promised yourself.*

*—Grateful Beast*

A few weeks later, I got a text from Beanstalk inviting me to come be a part of her photoshoot in my side of town. By this time, I almost forgot about the contest. I refused to go online to read the annoying chatter, comparisons and guesses. They might've already announced the winner for all I knew. She must've worked harder than me and deserved it. I planned to congratulate her whole-heartedly.

I wanted to treat Beanstalk to lunch, but I knew I had wiped out my credit cards on the contest. I checked my bank just to see—$1.07—yup, I was broke. I just hoped Beanstalk wouldn't ask to eat out somewhere. I couldn't even pay for myself, much less the both of us. I felt so guilty and embarrassed.

# TRANSFORMATION CHAMP

I walked up to her hotel excited to see her in person. When she opened the door, she didn't hug me immediately. She was awkward-nervous but smiling.

In slow motion I looked around the room. I saw a bright light behind her, a boom mic, a huge camera, six other young, healthy, and buff people all staring at me, and another huge camera . . .

"Congratulations, Nina! Bodybuilding.com and Dymatize Nutrition have chosen you as the winner of the 2015 Bodybuilding.com Transformation Challenge."

Leaping into the air, I screamed, "OH MY GOD!!!"

I'd already won for myself. Now I was winning for the world.

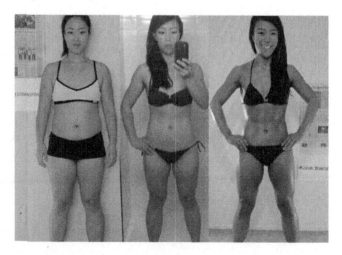

*Starting from left: "Before," "Halfway," and "After" (the original raw submitted pics)*

# EPILOGUE

P.S. Remember how I asked myself often, what was the purpose of all this eating like a bird, exercising like a beast, losing my period, whining, praying, and being dramatic as hell? The purpose was to teach me to always hold onto FAITH and FOCUS with everything I've got. Despite all my fears, my doubts, my mean thoughts and my imperfections, as long as I do my best to hold onto faith and focus till the very end, I am guaranteed to win.

# REFERENCES

1. Allison Kim, "2015 Bodybuilding.com $200,000 Transformation Challenge Winners Announced," *Bodybuilding.com*, June 2, 2015, www.globenewswire.com/news-release/2015/06/02/741476/10137006/en/201 5-BODYBUILDING-COM-200-000-TRANSFORMATION-CHALLENGE-WINNERS-ANNOUNCED.html

2. *Accepted*. Directed by Steve Pink (2006; Universal City, CA: Universal Pictures), Film.

3. "Samsung Galaxy 3—Amazing Funny Commercial," YouTube video, 1:00, posted by Jack Angel, February 19, 2013, www.youtube.com/watch?v=2DCNMccBQM4.

4. Kevin Cook, "Playboy Profile: Manny Pacquiao," *Playboy Entertainment for All*, October 17, 2011, www.playboy.com/articles/playboy-profile-manny-pacquiao.

5. Amy Edmondson, "Strategies for Learning from Failure," *Harvard Business Review*, April 2011, www.hbr.org/2011/04/strategies-for-learning-from-failure.

6. Ibid.

7. J.D. Meier, "How to Develop a Psychology of Resilience," *Time*, March 16, 2016, www.time.com/4256436/resilience/.

# ACKNOWLEDGMENTS

Winning was not my doing. The effort was mine, but I won because of the help of everything and everyone around me. And that's how this story was even possible.

Thank you awesome God!

Thank you successful reader!

Thank you so much Bodybuilding.com, Coach Beanstalk, my editor Nancy Pile, my family, friends, mentors, students, and generous sponsors who supported me!

# ABOUT THE AUTHOR

You were made for great success! Nina Nam doesn't care if you thought that was random for her author bio, because it is the truth. Trusting that great things always come, won her $80,000 as the grand prizewinner of Bodybuilding.com's annual 12-week Transformation Challenge in 2015.

Nina hosted one of the biggest health and fitness expos in the country, the Fit Expo. She taught cardio-kickboxing group fitness classes at Equinox and 24 Hour Fitness. She studied premed and theatre arts at the University of California Berkeley.

Ask her anything on Instagram @theninanam. Come to her uplifting events and find out about her next shenanigan: www.ninanam.com.

Made in the USA
Monee, IL
27 June 2021

71984851R00090